A VOLUME IN THE CENSUS MONOGRAPH SERIES

AMERICAN AGRICULTURE

Its Structure and Place in the Economy

by

RONALD L. MIGHELL

Agricultural Economist
Agricultural Research Service
U. S. Department of Agriculture

for the
SOCIAL SCIENCE RESEARCH COUNCIL
in cooperation with the
U. S. DEPARTMENT OF AGRICULTURE
AGRICULTURAL RESEARCH SERVICE
and the
U. S. DEPARTMENT OF COMMERCE
BUREAU OF THE CENSUS

JOHN WILEY & SONS, INC., NEW YORK
CHAPMAN & HALL, LIMITED, LONDON

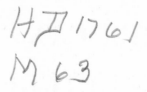

Library of Congress Catalog Card Number: 55-8179

PRINTED IN THE UNITED STATES OF AMERICA

FOREWORD

The statistical results compiled by the Bureau of the Census constitute a tremendous mass of detailed information about the population of
the United States and its characteristics and economic activities. To
meet the requirements of government agencies, business concerns, and
investigators of social problems and to satisfy the needs of individual
citizens, facts must be gathered and published, showing the distribution
of the population in each large and small political unit with respect to
age, sex, color, marital status, occupation, income, education, national
origin, and other characteristics. This information provides the basis
for apportionment of representatives in Congress, for answering many
questions by direct reference, and for formulating many plans, at least
in preliminary form.

It is the first business of the Bureau of the Census to put into print
the census results that directly answer as many such questions as possible. Along with these results, similar data from one or two previous
censuses are usually included. Limitations of time, space, and money
prevent any extensive statement of the relations between particular results, the long-term trends of significant totals and subtotals, the shifting proportions of the people belonging to different categories, various
interesting and important relations such as those between income, occupation, and age. It is not that the Bureau of the Census fails in any
sense to appreciate the value and need for such analyses, but rather
that it must concentrate on its basic concern with the summary statistics
that constitute its unique contribution to knowledge.

When plans for the 1950 Census were made, the need for more extensive analysis was recognized and a series of census monographs similar
to those issued after the 1920 Census was proposed. Because of the
pressures caused by the depression in the early 1930's and by defense
and war in the early 1940's, plans for monographs based on those censuses could not be carried out. Late in the 1940's interested persons
from business, research, and government agencies expressed the need
for a series that would provide analyses of the most significant results
of the 1950 Census. The Social Science Research Council, with the assistance of Russell Sage Foundation, took the lead in stimulating the
formulation of suitable plans and in June 1950 appointed a Committee
on Census Monographs to cooperate with the Bureau in organizing this
project. The members of the Committee are:

Ralph G. Hurlin, Russell Sage Foundation (Chairman)

Robert W. Burgess, formerly Western Electric Company, since February 1953 Director of the Bureau of the Census

John D. Durand, United Nations

Ernest M. Fisher, Columbia University

F. F. Hill, Cornell University

Frederick F. Stephan, Princeton University

Conrad Taeuber, Bureau of the Census

Ralph J. Watkins, Dun & Bradstreet, Inc.

Paul Webbink, Social Science Research Council

J. Frederic Dewhurst, Twentieth Century Fund, and William F. Ogburn, University of Chicago, were members of the Committee during the first year and a half.

It is essential in any sound census monograph program to obtain the cooperation of authors with a broad understanding not only of the statistical information provided by the regular tabulations of the current census but also of the results of earlier censuses and other relevant knowledge and points of view from other sources and even from other countries. The preparation of a monograph should include broad exploration of new questions suggested by the new information, as well as narrowing the elements of doubt and controversy on old questions. The Social Science Research Council Committee early undertook, in consultation with leading figures in various professional fields, to develop a suggested list of monograph titles and authors and persuaded experts in the subject areas selected to undertake the preparation of memoranda outlining and discussing the topics proposed. Then, in 1951, arrangements were made for continuing cooperation between the Committee and the Bureau concerning the selection of topics, proposals of authors and consultants, and editorial supervision.

Throughout the conduct of the project there has been close collaboration with a number of interested Federal agencies and with universities and research organizations, which provided staff and facilities to help bring the project to completion. They and the Council, which also obtained necessary funds from the Rockefeller and Russell Sage Foundations, provided assistance without which the monographs could not have been prepared.

The task of preparing monographs is an essential part of the broad function of making the information secured by censuses fully available to satisfy the needs and interests of the community and to constitute a broad base for further studies in the social sciences. As Director of the Census and President of the Social Science Research Council, respectively, we wish to record our full approval of the monograph project. It is not implied, of course, that the views expressed in these reports are necessarily those of the Bureau of the Census, the Department of Commerce, or the Social Science Research Council. The views are those of the individual authors, each of whom has been given the freedom to interpret available materials in the light of his technical knowledge and competence. This freedom of the individual authors is an essential element in making the most useful analyses and interpretations generally available to the community.

ROBERT W. BURGESS, DIRECTOR
BUREAU OF THE CENSUS

PENDLETON HERRING, PRESIDENT
SOCIAL SCIENCE RESEARCH COUNCIL

March, 1955

PREFACE

This book is addressed to readers who are interested in agriculture, but who are not necessarily professional agricultural specialists. Its purpose is to present in ordinary words a picture of the structure of agriculture, of its separate parts, of how these parts are assembled, and of how the whole fits into the economy of the Nation.

An understanding of the midcentury status of farms and farm people is essential for an informed citizen who wishes to understand public issues related to production and consumption of food, fiber, and other products of farm origin. This book does not attempt to present a solution to pressing problems, to furnish forecasts, or to provide a sudden spur to action. It does seek to provide a solid platform from which others may launch forth on such specific assignments.

Misconceptions about the structure of agriculture are common for several reasons. The people of the United States are now largely urban; most of them do not have the daily contact with farming that they have with other occupations. Farm people themselves do not always appreciate the interlocking relationships between agriculture and other sectors of the economy.

Much of the difficulty arises from the human tendency to see the current picture not as it actually is, but as it was some time ago. Mental images formed earlier are retained. All of us need to be on guard to avoid seeing current events through the windows of yesterday. It is as though we carried about with us mental television screens equipped with sets of colorful old films, and, when we think we are seeing the world as it is, some psychological circuit closes and we are merely rerunning well-worn films out of the past. Our preconceived ideas of things prevent us from seeing them as they actually are. The familiar mental picture comes between us and the actual object, character, or event.

This book is intended to help us televise new pictures and cut new sound tracks for our mental television screens and to bring up to date our preconceptions. Then as we approach current farm problems they may be placed against the background of today rather than that of yesterday.

Visitors from abroad are often astonished by the mobility and freedom of movement of Americans. The relative absence of class barriers, the universality of educational facilities, the breadth of economic opportunities are strange to them. Rural and urban people are becoming more and more alike with respect to their well-being, their outlook, their economic opportunities, their participation in the total life of the community. Even our own people are not fully aware of how far the last half century has taken us in the direction of an integrated economy and society.

Not all the changes in our national life are good. Here and there social and economic strains and stresses need attention. Conflicts in viewpoints frequently erect barriers to solutions. More carefully drawn summaries of fact and reality will help to remove some of the controversial elements and will assist in reaching conclusions.

This analysis is based mainly on the 1950 Census of Agriculture and related materials prepared in the Bureau of the Census, U. S. Department of Commerce, and in the Agricultural Research Service and the Agricultural Marketing Service, U. S. Department of Agriculture, some jointly and some separately.

An advisory committee on "The Structure of American Agriculture" has been helpful both in developing the initial plan for the report and throughout the analysis. Members of the committee are: Conrad Taeuber and Ray Hurley, Bureau of the Census; D. Gale Johnson and W. E. Hendrix, University of Chicago; Herrell F. DeGraff, Cornell University; Howard W. Beers, University of Kentucky; Donald R. Murphy, *Wallace's Farmer* and *Iowa Homestead;* Howard R. Tolley, Ford Foundation; Walter W. Wilcox, Library of Congress; and Phillip F. Aylesworth, Office of the Secretary, Foster F. Elliott, Agricultural Marketing Service, and Sherman E. Johnson (Chairman of the Committee), Agricultural Research Service, United States Department of Agriculture.

Acknowledgment of the assistance of many other persons is prevented by reasons of space, but a special debt is owed to my fellow staff members of the Production Economics Research Branch of the Agricultural Research Service.

RONALD L. MIGHELL

Washington, D. C.
March, 1955

CONTENTS

CHAPTER 1

AGRICULTURE TODAY AND YESTERDAY

In a very real sense, the long story of mankind is written in the wood, stone, and metal from which working tools were fashioned. For untold centuries these were mainly hand tools, devices for using human muscle more efficiently. The application of power to accomplish useful work is only one side of technological progress, though perhaps the most spectacular one.

For most of these centuries, civilization advanced on the sweating, aching backs of humankind. Even free men were slaves to unremitting toil to achieve the bare minimum of subsistence. The arts of peace and the arts of war alike depended on the direct application of manpower. Several times in history, the appearance of a new source of mobile power has revolutionized agriculture. One such occasion was the substitution of oxpower for some of the manpower, another was the advent of horsepower, and a third was the introduction of mechanical power. The successful harnessing of water, wind, and electricity— sources of stationary power—represented parallel advances.

Power revolutions affected urban industry and agriculture in different ways. Advances in stationary power were usually of more benefit in mines and factories than on farms. Innovations in mobile power were necessary before corresponding benefits could be gained on farms. The dispersed nature of farming operations, in both space and time, is primarily responsible for this difference.

The burst of invention and progress since 1800, known as the "Industrial Revolution," pushed forward the material civilization of the Western World markedly. Changes in our own rural and urban population during this period (fig. 1-1) illustrate one result of this process. In 1800, this country was essentially rural. By 1950, more than half the population was urban, and most of the nonfarm rural people who lived in towns and villages were more urban in their way of living than were the city people of 1800.

The Industrial Revolution enlarged the market for food and fiber. A larger market meant that farmers could specialize to some extent and could use labor more effectively. Crops could be grown on better-adapted soils. Fields could be enlarged; crop rotations and livestock

1

systems could be established. Improved husbandry could be followed.
But for a long time the technology that revolutionized urban factories
and provided railroads and highways changed life on the farm very
little. Spinning, weaving, and other home industries were removed from
farms to factories, but the rest of farm life and work went on as before.

Farm tools and equipment in daily use had changed little for hun-

FIGURE 1-1. URBAN AND RURAL POPULATION, 1790 TO 1950

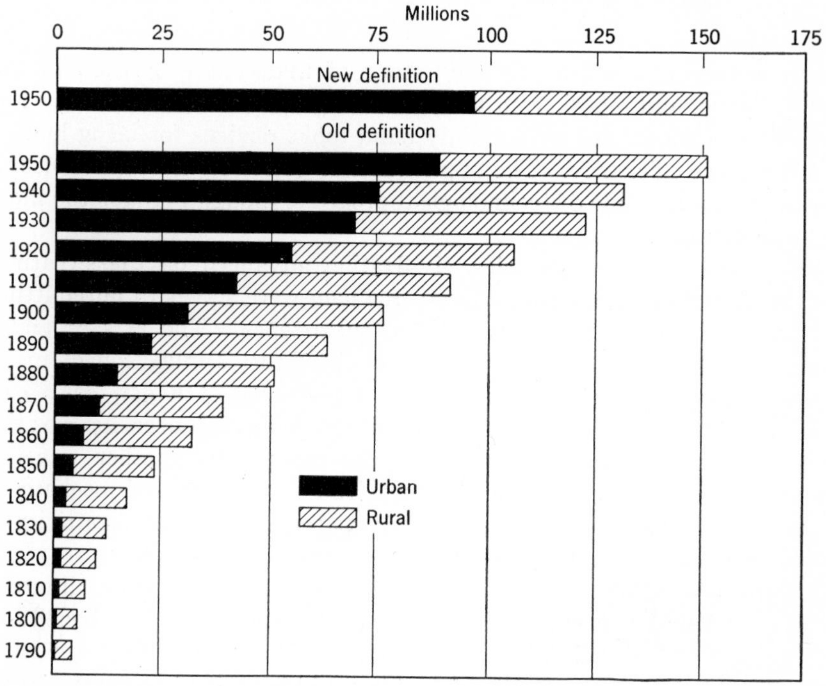

Source: Bureau of the Census.

dreds of years. Although men had used horses for riding and for
military purposes for a long time, they were not much used for farm
draft purposes. Oxen furnished the chief draft power for plowing
throughout the Middle Ages and up through colonial times in this
country.

The first half of the nineteenth century was the period of the axe
and the hoe; the second half, the period of horse-drawn machinery; and
the 50 years from 1900 to 1950, the period of mechanical power. Perhaps we are now entering the period of chemical marvels. Not until
the end of each of these past periods had full advantage been taken of
the possibilities available.

Farm machinery, as we understand it, is hardly more than a century
old. By 1840,

The sickle of colonial days had virtually given way to modified types of the scythe and the grain cradle. In 1837, farmers were enthusiastic about the better cradles that were used in parts of the East; and the American scythe of that period, with its longer and thinner blade, was much used for several years after mowing machines were in the fields. Crude as the machines and tools of that time were, compared with current models, they represented a long step forward from the beginning of the century.

Many makes of farm machines were tried out before 1850. Farm machines of the local blacksmith shop were being replaced by factory-made machines with wide commercial distribution. McCormick's reaper was becoming a reality. Portable horse-drawn power units and threshing machines were seen. The fanning mill, through with its critical period of experimentation, was in general use for cleaning grain. Horse-drawn mowing machines were at work in the hay fields. Shovel cultivators were replacing many steel hoes, and the steel walking plow was a few years old.[1]

Horse-drawn machinery was not perfected until the latter half of the nineteenth century. The internal combustion engine came around the turn of the century, but it was not until 1920 that farm tractors began

FIGURE 1-2. HORSES AND MULES, AND TRACTORS ON FARMS, JANUARY 1, 1910 TO 1954

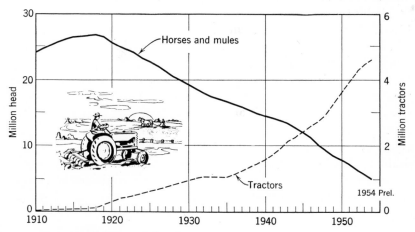

Source: Agricultural Research Service.

to appear in numbers and that substitution of tractors for horses and mules began in earnest (fig. 1-2). The transition was delayed until such innovations as the tractor-drawn row-crop cultivator and other equipment designed for tractor power were introduced. The coming of rubber to the farm in the 1930's speeded up the rate of tractor travel beyond the walking speed of men and horses. By 1950, horseless farming was a realized fact on nearly half the farms in the United States.

[1] Martin R. Cooper, Glen T. Barton, and Albert P. Brodell, "Progress of Farm Mechanization," U. S. Dept. Agr. Misc. Pub. 630, Oct. 1947, p. 6.

Since the turn of the century

A recent book by Frederick Lewis Allen, *The Big Change,* considers the manifold changes in this country in the last half century.[2] Population doubled; per capita income rose; customs, habits, and ways of life probably changed more in these 50 years than in any other time or place. Despite two major wars, a major depression, and other events, the process of change goes on and the pace appears to be accelerating. Mr. Allen's book devotes little space to farmers as such, but much of what he says applies to them as well as to city people. In fact, the "big change" has been an even "bigger change" for farm people. Consider just the matter of "isolation," which explained much of the former differences between country and city life and customs. Only those who are old enough to remember the kind of world revealed in Whittier's *Snow-Bound* or Marie Sandoz's *Old Jules* can appreciate the one-time isolation and loneliness of country life. Today, except for scattered pockets, one must go to the Arctic, the upper Amazon, the South Seas, or some equally remote corner of the earth to find anything like the old isolation, and even then he will probably keep in touch with the world outside by radio.[3]

In 1900, the isolation of the farmer and particularly the farmer's wife was nearly as complete as it had been in 1800. Rural free delivery of mail had just started (1896) as had installation of the first telephones. As the twentieth century moved along, the Model T, improved highways, airways, radio, electricity, movies, television, and other elements joined to complete the revolution in transportation and communication. Education, both formal and informal, became available to urban and rural people alike. Only a few cultural islands remain within this country, and these are being whittled away as economic opportunities are opened to their people. Such islands are explained by factors other than space and distance; they are about as likely to be found in cities as in rural areas.

Changes in farm production since 1900 [4]

No one word in the language can convey what has happened to our agriculture in the 50 years just past. "Change" is a colorless term that fails to suggest the bewildering variety of happenings. "Trend" may imply too continuous and powerful direction. Perhaps "development" comes nearest to suggesting the expanding and unfolding nature of the transformations in this fruitful half-century. As Schultz points out

2 Frederick Lewis Allen, *The Big Change,* Harper and Brothers, New York, 1952.

3 On the other side of the Iron Curtain, time has slipped backward in certain respects and communication is less complete.

4 See especially the analysis of changes in the report by Sherman E. Johnson, "Changes in American Farming," *U. S. Dept. Agr. Misc. Pub. 707,* Dec. 1949.

"There is no received theory explaining economic development comparable, for example, to the theory of the firm" in explaining the functioning of the business firm under static conditions.[5]

Economists and other specialists alike have groped for an understanding of the nature of the action and reaction between agriculture and the rest of the economy. That expansion was the major keynote in all sectors during this period there can be no doubt. But developments were not altogether smooth and continuous. Episodic changes were

FIGURE 1-3. FARM OUTPUT AND LABOR INPUT, 1910 TO 1953

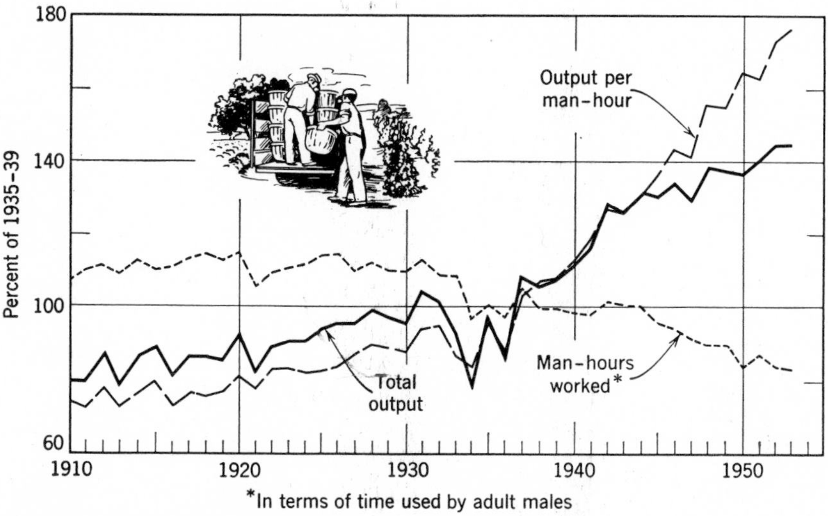

Source: Agricultural Research Service.

frequent. Cyclical storms on the economic seas raged from time to time. Several major wars occurred.

The aggregate change in agriculture in terms of production is reflected in the index of farm output (fig. 1-3). From 1910 to 1950, farm output rose about 75 percent. The course of this index through the years tells much about the path of agricultural progress. Up until 1930 a continuous but modest over-all expansion is apparent. The reductions in the 1930's are related mainly to drought but partly also to depression. Expansion in the 1940's came at a much more rapid rate under the favorable demand conditions of wartime and the pressure of food needs.

5 Theodore W. Schultz, *The Economic Organization of Agriculture*, McGraw-Hill Book Co., New York, 1953, pp. 3, 148. Economists recognize the statement presented by Joseph A. Schumpeter in his *Theory of Economic Development*, Harvard University Press, 1936, as perhaps the leading theory that has been advanced in this field. But this and other theories have not yet been formalized and received as adequate explanations of the process of economic development in its entirety.

One can place a ruler on the chart from 1920 to 1950 and find that the 1920's and the 1940's lie almost in the same line of ascent. But if the whole period from 1910 is considered, it appears that the rate of increase since 1940 is considerably more rapid.

Reasons underlying this expansion of output varied from one time to another. Expanding domestic markets and shrinking foreign outlets represented fundamental economic forces at work on the demand side during much of the period. Yet there were ebbs and flows—domestic demand stood still during the depression of the 1930's, and foreign demand rose sharply in the World War II and postwar period.

On the supply side, until 1920, the main explanation for expansion was the continuing occupation and development of new land resources. By 1920, nearly all these possibilities were exhausted except for limited areas to be developed through irrigation and drainage.

Since 1920 and especially since 1940, technology in one form or another has been the source of most of the additional output. Higher yields of crops and livestock have come through improved methods of farming, and through higher inputs of fertilizer, feed, and other resources. Between 1918 and 1953, substitution of tractor power for horse and mule power released about 70 million acres of land formerly used to produce feed for draft animals. These acres now can be used to produce food crops and feed for food-producing livestock. The transfer from animal to mechanical power began about 1918; from then on it was more or less continuous (fig. 1-2).

The new applied technology in agriculture had its origin mainly in the research work of federal and state agricultural experiment stations, although private individuals and business concerns played their role, too. Technicians in farm machinery and equipment companies have supplied much of the inventive genius needed for development of farm machinery and equipment. But publicly supported research has supplied the greater part of the invention and discovery that lies at the source of the stream of applied technology in agriculture.

It is necessary here to distinguish between the kinds of productive activity included in original research and invention and the technological development involved in the manufacture and marketing of an item already discovered or invented. The role of industry in the second kind of activity is significant. Sometimes the research and development phases are so interwoven that they cannot be separated. Henry Ford, for example, put together several existing inventions and worked out an application of assembly-line methods. In this way he brought about the first mass production of a low-cost automobile that people of ordinary means could afford to buy. Perhaps that was really social invention; certainly it was technology in application.

The contribution of technology to farm production can be only partly measured by reviewing some outstanding instances. One remembers, in recent times, hybrid corn which increased corn yields 20 percent; farther back, invention of the Babcock test for butterfat which helped to revolutionize dairy production and marketing; measures developed to stamp out cattle-tick fever; means found for controlling the cotton boll weevil; and, in the last 15 years, discoveries in incubation, breeding, and feeding which together brought the commercial-broiler industry

FIGURE 1-4. TRENDS IN EATING HABITS (PER CAPITA CIVILIAN CONSUMPTION), 1911 TO 1950, AND PROJECTIONS TO 1975

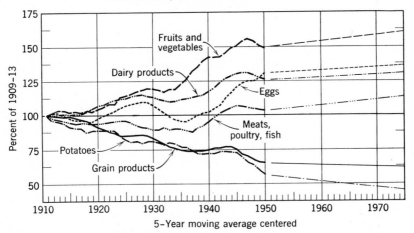

5-Year moving average centered

Source: Agricultural Marketing Service.

into being. These are only a few of the examples that could be listed, in production, marketing, transportation, utilization, and food preservation.

But more than research is needed to get new technology into use. Early efforts to get improved methods before farmers culminated in the legislation that established the cooperative federal-state agricultural extension service program in 1914. This service was expanded following World War I. After 1920, its influence was increasingly felt. Extension education began to shorten appreciably the period between the discovery of new methods and their widespread adoption by farmers.

The progress of general secondary school education in rural areas and the organization of vocational agriculture courses in high schools, together with the formation of 4-H Boys' and Girls' Clubs and other youth organizations, also became influential.

But, as farm production expanded, the number of people on farms shrank. Between 1910 and 1950, the farm population fell from 32 to 24 million, or one-fourth. The 13.6 million farm workers on farms in 1910 dropped more than a third. Actual man-hours worked decreased about a fourth. As a result output per man-hour more than doubled.

Not only did aggregate farm output increase about 75 percent between 1910 and 1950, but its composition changed, so that its real
value to consumers is greater. Take the food we eat. In fig. 1-4 the
trends in our eating habits since 1910 are sketched out for the major
food groups. Our diets are richer in fruits and vegetables, dairy
products, and eggs—foods that contain nutrients that were most lacking in the diets of 1910. Cereals and potatoes are now eaten in smaller
quantities. The change in occupational status from outdoor to indoor
types of work and the lower need for high-caloric foods partly explain
this. But the main thing is that these foods had to make room for
more nutritious foods.

Relative significance of new technology and inputs

The increase in output from 1910 to 1950 was not costless as new
methods were applied. Net output has not increased as much as total
output. The question therefore arises as to how much of the total
increase can be attributed to new and better techniques and how much
to additional inputs. The most carefully derived estimates in this matter were developed by Schultz, using data and assistance from the
Production Economics Research Branch, Agricultural Research Service.[6]
The findings of his analysis indicate that roughly from one-half to
three-fourths of the increase in output can be attributed to technology
alone. The difference between the two fractions is a matter of technical
construction of index numbers. Use of terminal-period prices as weights
gave the higher fraction, and beginning-year weights the lower fraction.

That part of the increase that is due to improved technology has cost
the community something in expenditures for research, education, and
diffusion of knowledge. But this cost is only a small fraction of the
value of the benefits society received. Schultz points out, for example,
that the estimated value of inputs saved in 1 year as a result of improved techniques is more than the expenditures for agricultural research and extension work of all Federal and State Governments since
1910.[7]

An additional social benefit lies in the labor supply for industrial
expansion that agriculture has been able to furnish as a result of improved technology. In the past, immigration and a tendency at times
for labor to be released from agriculture more rapidly than industrial
opportunities became available tended to mask the tremendous social
gain involved in this process. Without such a reservoir of manpower
our economy doubtless would have evolved more slowly. Experience in
other regions, for example, in present-day Australia, suggests that too
limited a labor potential may check economic progress.

6 Schultz, *op. cit.*, pp. 109 and 120.
7 Schultz, *ibid.*, p. 120.

C H A P T E R 2

AGRICULTURE IN THE TOTAL
ECONOMIC PROCESS

How large a place does agriculture occupy in the whole economy? How does it fit into the total economic process in relation to the productive activities involved in transforming raw materials into intermediate and then into final consumer goods and services? These questions are not easy to answer. In a complex economy like ours, it is difficult to separate, even for analytical purposes, a single industry such as agriculture from the total economic matrix in which it is imbedded.

We draw rather arbitrary lines across the flow of production and say that what happens on farms is agriculture. Yet we are concerned also with the prefarm sources of production goods—machines, fertilizer, supplies—used in agriculture. And we are nearly always thinking about the marketing and the processing of farm products. It is clear that agricultural interests go beyond the farm boundaries. This division between what happens on farms and what takes place off farms suggests two ways of gauging agriculture's place in the total economy. In this chapter we shall look at agriculture from both these viewpoints. It is important to do so because either alone may lead to confusion and misunderstanding. Many activities once conducted on farms or in farm homes were transferred to the nonfarm sphere because they could be more efficiently handled there. But transfer from farms to city factories or processing plants does not mean complete elimination of a given function. When we think of a farmer riding a tractor we must remember the men who work in the tractor factory and the men who produce the oil and gas to keep the machine going.

Agriculture—internal phase

The relative size of agriculture within farm boundaries can be measured in several different ways. An aggregate measure of all resources used on farms compared with a similar measure of all resources used in the whole economy might be the best way. But simpler measures will serve our purpose. Perhaps the most useful are in terms of people: the proportion of the total population living on farms, the proportion of employed workers on farms, and the percentage of net national income derived from farming or received by farm people.

9

In 1950, about 16.6 percent of our population lived on farms, but, as the farm population contains more children and old people, only about 12.2 percent of all employed persons worked on farms.[1] The part of the national income derived from farming was approximately 8 percent; but farm people received about 9.5 percent of the national income. This figure was arrived at after adjusting for nonfarm income received by farm people and farm income received by city people. Income data are not quite satisfactory for this comparison, because of technical difficulties and differences in environment between farm and urban life. The purchasing power of farm dollars is somewhat higher because farmers have more opportunity than city dwellers to buy at points in the marketing chain where margins and prices are lower. Some economists have estimated that the purchasing power of farm dollars should be reckoned as 25 percent higher than that of city dollars. If this were accepted as further adjustment we might say that nearly 12 percent of the national income is received by farmers.

Even so, average per capita real income appears to be somewhat lower for farm people than for those in other occupations. Reasons for this are discussed later.

In any case the *relative* significance of agriculture measured inside farm fence lines has been greatly reduced since 1910. In terms of population and percentage of national income it has diminished by half.

Year	Percentage of population on farms	Percentage of national income from agriculture
1910	34.9	16.0
1920	30.1	14.0
1930	24.9	8.3
1940	23.2	8.1
1950	16.6	8.0

Agriculture—external phase and over-all

The proportion of the total population that is counted as rural is sometimes considered a rough index of the total influence of agriculture. But many rural people, although they live near the open country and may have roots in the soil, are urban minded and earn their living in urban ways.

[Probably a better way of looking at the over-all significance of agriculture is to consider production from the viewpoint of the consumer. Of all the goods and services that consumers in the United States bought in 1949, what part came from agriculture? Roughly half of all the money spent by consumers in that year was for food, clothing, and other products of farm origin] They spent about 26 percent of the total

---

[1] The 1950 Census classification by major occupation groups was used. A slightly higher proportion of all employed persons—13.5 percent—was counted in the farm population, because more farm people work at nonfarm jobs than nonfarm people do at farm jobs.

for food alone, 12 percent for clothing and other textiles, 9 percent for tobacco and domestic beverages, and probably several percentage points more for agricultural elements contained in other manufactured products, whose farm beginnings had vanished in complex industrial processes. Of course, all these products had many services added to them between farmer and consumer. They were transported, processed, incorporated with other products of nonfarm origin, and some were changed beyond any possibility of recognition. Some of the categories also included articles of nonfarm origin, like nylon and synthetic rubber, which supplement or replace farm products in certain uses.

But, after taking account of all the qualifications, one can say that a good half of all the goods and services that enter final consumption have farm origins.

The 1950 Census of Population provides some useful data on occupational status and numbers of employed persons by industries. These data are not classified in a way to permit direct calculation of the number of people employed at each stage in production of farm products, except for those employed on farms. But with the aid of other information some informal estimates can be made. These estimates are given in the accompanying tabulation in terms of percentages of the total number of employed workers.

Stage of production	Percentage of total number of employed workers
	Percent
Total...................	25.7
Prefarm...................	2.5
Farm...................	12.2
Postfarm, food industries............	7.0
Postfarm, textiles and other..........	4.0

From the viewpoint of workers employed in agriculture and related industries one can say that about a fourth of all employed workers in our labor force are included.

The farmer's share of the consumer's dollar

[Still another way of viewing the place of agriculture in the economy is to consider the concept of the farmer's share of the consumer's dollar] This works best with food items and in fig. 2-1 we see the respective shares received by farmers and by the marketing system in recent years.

[In 1949, for example, the farmer's share of the consumer's food dollar was about 49¢ in terms of a representative market basket of farm foods.] [For nonfood items like cotton, wool, and tobacco, similar computations show that the farmer's share averaged from 12 to 17¢.] For industrial products in which farm commodities are incorporated in minor proportions, the general concept becomes inappropriate. Automobiles, houses, chemicals, and the like, contain textiles, paints, and other items of farm origin in small quantities which are significant in the aggregate. If an approximate estimate could be made of the farmer's share in all farm-connected products bought by consumers, it might

FIGURE 2-1. FARM AND MARKETING SHARES IN RETAIL FOOD COSTS

[Data are for market basket of farm foods, based on average 1935–39 purchases for family of 3 average consumers]

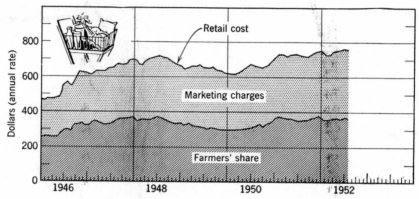

Source: Agricultural Marketing Service.

be something like a sixth. (This follows from our earlier conclusion that about half of all consumer's expenditures are for farm-connected items.) Taking account of the farmer's share of the dollars spent for food, for nonfood items, and allowing for industrial use of farm products, one arrives at an approximate one-sixth share for the aggregate of all.

Farm expenditures

In the sense used above, the farmer's share is a gross, not a net, share. Expenditures for farm supplies and inputs are still to be accounted for. We need to look carefully at farm expenses to understand the significance of the external prefarm sources of intermediate products. The movement of farm-produced items between farms must also be noted.

Use of intermediate products in agriculture has increased rapidly since 1910. In analyzing this question, Kendrick and Jones found that the value of intermediate products in constant dollars rose to a level more than four times as high in 1950 as in 1910, whereas output went up about 79 percent.[2]

Their estimates of intermediate products include farm-produced feeds, seeds, livestock, and other items transferred between farms. Thus they are somewhat too high to represent the interchange between the farm and

---

[2] John W. Kendrick and Carl E. Jones, "Gross National Farm Product in Constant Dollars, 1910–50," U. S. Dept. of Commerce, *Survey of Current Business*, Sept. 1951, pp. 13–19.

nonfarm sectors. But they do give us a correct picture of the increasing commercialization of farming.

In table 2-1 we have a comparison of the broad categories of farm expenses for 1910 and 1950. No adjustment was made for change in

TABLE 2-1.—FARM PRODUCTION EXPENSES, BY CLASSES, UNITED STATES, 1910 AND 1950

Item	1910	1950	1950 as a percentage of 1910
	Million dollars	*Million dollars*	*Percent*
Total gross farm income	7,543	32,989	437
Total production expenses	3,556	19,704	554
Hired labor	755	2,724	361
Net rent to nonfarm landlords	340	1,155	340
Operation of motor vehicles	7	1,900	27,143
Depreciation of motor vehicles	13	1,223	9,408
Seed purchased	56	536	957
Fertilizer and lime	149	938	630
Taxes on farm property	191	919	481
Depreciation of buildings	318	1,361	428
Depreciation of other machinery	353	1,453	412
Miscellaneous	545	1,792	329
Interest on farm-mortgage debt	203	264	130
Livestock purchased	200	2,051	1,026
Feed purchased	426	3,388	795

Source: Bureau of Agricultural Economics, "The Farm Income Situation," Sept.–Oct. 1953.

price level. But, from this table alone, some of the marked changes that occurred during the period may be observed. Outstanding is the immense increase in expenses for motor vehicles. Other items that increased much more than the average are feed, livestock, seed, and fertilizer and lime. Increases in expenses for interest, rent, labor, and miscellaneous items were well below the average. These changes reflect the advance of technology and the increasing mechanization of farming.

One should note that total production expenses amounted to about 47 percent of total gross farm income in 1910 and 60 percent in 1950. Percentages for selected years are given in the accompanying tabulation.

Year	*Percent*
1910	47
1920	55
1930	63
1940	59
1950	60

The age of technology has brought some increase in this relationship, but it is the qualitative change within the expense items that is impressive. The increases in expenses for motor vehicles and for feed, seed, and livestock purchased stand out.

Interdependent nature of agriculture

Agriculture is usually considered a basic or primary industry. Most of us accept this designation without thinking about it. Who can doubt that food, clothing, and related goods are basic necessities? But, unless we realize that the technological revolution in production has changed the meaning of primary industry, we shall fail to understand the true nature of present-day agriculture and its interdependence with other industries.

Agriculture as a way of production and as a way of life has undergone change beyond the usual comprehension. Our ideas lag behind the progress of events. And for excellent reasons. The light and shadow, the color of earlier times have been brightened and intensified by literary and artistic landmarks. Our impressions have been influenced by such cultural models as Edwin Markham's *Man with the Hoe,* and Grant Wood's *American Gothic (Farmer and His Wife).* Grandma Moses' paintings also preserve the story of the past. All these things keep before us a picture of Man wrestling with the raw forces of Nature with little more than bare hands and simple tools. Current ways of farming are as far removed from this former reality as are present-day engineering methods for constructing a modern office building from those used a half century ago.

An Austrian economist, Böhm-Bawerk, in the middle of the last century developed a classical description of the formation of capital goods which profoundly affected the thinking of economists. He used the expression "roundabout production" to convey his description of capitalistic processes as contrasted with primitive manual methods of work. Not all improved technology takes more capital goods, but, in general, technological progress means that more capital is invested and production becomes more roundabout. As this occurs, the period of time that elapses from the first step in any productive process until the final consumer's good is produced becomes longer, but efficiency becomes greater. Hybrid seed corn, for example, is much more productive than open-pollinated seed corn—even though it takes more time and more money to produce a bushel of hybrid seed corn.

As agricultural technology becomes more roundabout in this sense, it becomes more efficient, and it also becomes more interdependent with other industries. It does so in both directions—prefarm and postfarm. We can more readily perceive the postfarm phases of this phenomenon, and they are more obvious to those who are not farmers. New uses for farm products, whether for food, clothing, or industrial purposes, represent a significant field for further development.

But, as mentioned above, farmers also become increasingly dependent on nonfarm sources of inputs—of intermediate products for further processing. Much of the pressure of advancing technology necessarily involves this kind of roundaboutness.

The farm as a biological manufacturing plant. The preceding discussion leads one to the conclusion that farms have become rather complex biological manufacturing plants. In many respects, the technological organization of commercial farms is more intricate and involved than that of industrial plants. The main differences have to do with the scale of operations and the biological nature of the manufacturing process. Farmers, like other manufacturers, bring together various resources and materials and put them through their factories. To the extent that they are crop producers, their visible manufacturing plants consist of fields exposed to sunlight, rainfall, and natural elements. Here they place their genetic materials and add fertilizer, pesticides, and other inputs. They power-tool the soil, power-harvest the products, and take them to concentration points for packaging and shipment.

For livestock producers, other biological problems of growth and production and different kinds of production cycles are involved. Capital investment in buildings is likely to be heavier. The need for storing feed supplies may make the factory analogy even more apt. Some types of poultry and milk enterprises that are completely housed under one roof are even referred to as "factory-type" production.

CHAPTER 3

DIMENSIONS OF THE AGRICULTURAL PLANT

What we mean by the aggregate agricultural plant may be defined in more than one way. Often we think of the concept as meaning simply the basic land and natural resources used in farm production. In primitive agriculture, before capital goods were accumulated, there was little except land and labor. Many who are disturbed about the long-run outlook for the world's food supply are still inclined to think mainly in these terms. Such questions as: How many people can the earth feed? or Is there enough land to go around? are frequently discussed as though land were the only resource involved. Only a few generations separate us from the time and circumstances that gave so much credence to Malthus' thesis of the pressure of population on the food supply. Social memories of recurring periods of famine and the "niggardliness" of nature through the centuries are not quickly erased.

But, in the parts of the world in which material progress has been most marked, we must now think not only of land but of all the cooperating resources that enter into production. In a broad sense then, the agricultural plant may be thought of as including the aggregate of land, labor, and capital goods (the great triad of resources) used in agriculture.[1]

In appraising the dimensions of the various resources used in agriculture, we must not give undue weight to the more durable goods, of which land itself is most durable. In any inventory process the durables loom up because their current valuation is the sum of the present values of their anticipated future uses. Even though the values of future uses are discounted, durability assures a current inventory value that is higher than the value of current use.

At the outset, therefore, let us check our statistical vision by considering the views framed by two separate accounting windows. The first window is called the "Balance Sheet of Agriculture," and the second is labeled the "Annual Flow of Resources Used in Agriculture." Like most windows, each of these was designed with a special frame and

---

[1] The term "plant" is used in this broad sense in the absence of a more suitable word, although "plant" usually refers to the fixed physical resources as distinguished from labor and variable resources.

placement so that it opens on a particular but partial view of the landscape. Each view will help us to evaluate the dimensions of the agricultural plant.

A *balance sheet* is simply a static appraisal of assets and claims at a given moment in time. It shows the net worth or position of the business, but it reveals little more than that. Successive snapshots through this window will show how the position has changed. This sort of serial

FIGURE 3-1. BALANCE SHEET OF AGRICULTURE, 1940 TO 1953

[Data are as of January 1 each year]

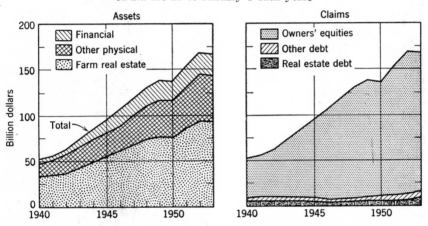

Source: Agricultural Research Service.

exposure is presented in fig. 3-1 for 1940–53.[2] The *annual flow* of resources used in production goes further; it measures the relative magnitude of each production input that joins the stream of production resources used in a year. From this we get information as to the working structure of the business and the relative contribution of the several resources. Each accounting window furnishes a different but an essential profile.

The "Balance Sheet of Agriculture" provides us with a grand summary of the assets and liabilities of agriculture looked at as one large enterprise. It is in effect a consolidated balance sheet of all farms, and it covers the interests of all groups in farming, as well as the financial assets of people who live on farms. A simplified summary of the Balance Sheet for January 1, 1950, is presented in table 3-1.

The picture of assets presented by the balance sheet shows a landscape dominated by real estate. But we must remember that real estate is a complex of land, buildings, and other land improvements. Esti-

---

2 Note that the upward trends in aggregate assets and liabilities are related to rising price levels in these years. The valuations are not bookkeeping values in the usual accounting sense but they reflect current changes in prices as well as in real quantities.

TABLE 3-1.—BALANCE SHEET OF AGRICULTURE, JANUARY 1, 1950

Assets	Amount	Claims	Amount
	Billion dollars		*Billion dollars*
Total......................	137	Total......................	137
Physical assets:		Liabilities:	
Real estate....................	76	Real-estate debt................	6
Non-real estate.................	41	Non-real-estate debt............	7
Financial assets...................	20	Proprietors' equities.............	124

Source: Bureau of Agricultural Economics, "The Balance Sheet of Agriculture, 1953," *U. S. Dept. Agr. Inf. Bul. 115*, Sept. 1953.

mates of the value of buildings apart from the land are available for census years. As indicated in table 3-2, the percentage that buildings comprise of the total real estate has risen since 1900; in 1950, buildings made up 28 percent of the total. If it were possible to take separate account of other land improvements—roads, fences, tile drains, irrigation ditches, etc.—the percentage of capital goods incorporated in the real estate would be still higher.

TABLE 3-2.—VALUE OF ALL FARM REAL ESTATE AND VALUE OF FARM BUILDINGS, CENSUS YEARS, 1900 TO 1950

Year	Value of all farm real estate [1]	Value of farm buildings only [2]	Farm buildings as a percentage of all farm real estate
	Billion dollars	*Billion dollars*	*Percent*
1900......	16.6	3.6	22
1910......	34.8	6.3	18
1920......	66.3	11.5	17
1930......	47.9	12.9	27
1940......	33.6	10.4	31
1950......	75.3	21.2	28

[1] Data on total value of land and buildings from *U. S. Census of Agriculture: 1950*, Vol. 2, *General Report*, p. 48.

[2] Data on value of farm buildings for 1900–1940 from *U. S. Census of Agriculture: 1940*, Vol. 3, *General Report*, p. 35; separate value of farm buildings not obtained in 1950 Census. Value of farm buildings for 1950 from Production Economics Research Branch, "Current Developments in the Farm Real Estate Market," *Agricultural Research Service Processed Report CD-37*, March 1954.

Non-real-estate physical assets include machinery and equipment, livestock, feed, and other supplies on hand. If these items and the financial assets could be put with the buildings and the capital improvements imbedded in the land, it is probable that their combined value would be about twice that of the bare land itself. In other words, capital goods and financial assets represent about two-thirds and bare land about one-third of the value of all agricultural assets.

The view from the second window shows the dimensions of the annual flow of each of the several categories of resources (table 3-3). The

TABLE 3-3.—RELATIVE QUANTITIES OF INPUTS USED IN AGRICULTURE, UNITED STATES, 1945–1948

Inputs	Percentage of total inputs
	Percent
Total inputs.............	100.0
Labor [1]...................	44.9
Land [2]..................	24.4
Interest [3]...............	5.0
Taxes [4].................	2.8
Depreciation [5]...........	9.9
Operation of motor vehicles...	6.0
Fertilizer and lime..........	2.6
Miscellaneous items.........	4.4

[1] Total farm labor, including value of unpaid operator and family labor. Hence returns for management and for risk bearing are in this item.

[2] Net rent on land and buildings.

[3] Interest on investment in non-real-estate items, including horses and mules, motor vehicles, other machinery, crops, and livestock.

[4] Taxes on farm property. They can be considered payments for inputs provided by public authority, as for example, highways. Farm property taxes are also used to pay for public services, like schools, that are not properly farm inputs. On the other hand, other kinds of taxes are used to provide public services that *are* farm inputs. Therefore, property taxes may serve as a rough index of farm inputs from public services.

[5] Depreciation of buildings, motor vehicles, machinery, and equipment, including that fraction (currently 40 percent) of automobiles assigned to farm-business use.

Source: Unpublished data from Production Economics Research Branch, Agricultural Research Service. Actual quantities of inputs, 1945–1948, weighted by 1946–1948 prices.

frame around this profile differs from that around the balance sheet in several ways. All production factors, including labor, are in this view. Durability does not affect the value of the quantities used, as it does the value of stocks of assets. Here we have only the quantities of each resource used up in a year's time in the production process.

This view brings out the significance of human labor in agriculture, accounting as it does for about 45 percent of all inputs and leading all other factors.

The second largest input listed in table 3-3 is land and buildings at nearly 25 percent of the total. Other resource items taken together make up the remaining 30 percent of all inputs. These items include the expenses associated with capital goods and supplies. In this classification again, the agricultural land item is a combined net rent total for land and buildings because of the difficulty of working out a satisfactory separation. If one were to attempt to estimate the building element (including other land improvements) the proportion of the net rent item for land and buildings to be allocated to land would be about the same as for the real estate assets in the balance sheet. This is because the depreciation item for buildings, which reflects the difference in durability of land and buildings, is included in the depreciation line. Possibly the input of bare land in a year makes up no more than 18 percent of the total inputs. On this basis we might arrange the triad of resources in the annual flow of inputs used in agriculture about as tabulated.

	Percent
Land................	18
Labor..............	45
Capital items.......	37
	100

To recapitulate in terms of physical and financial assets (excluding labor), bare land makes up roughly a third of the total and capital items nearly two-thirds. In terms of annual flows (including labor), land represents nearly a fifth of the total, labor more than two-fifths, and the capital complement more than a third of all inputs used in agriculture. Thus today land plays a considerably smaller aggregate, although a very essential, role in agriculture. But it is the large complement of capital goods that contributes to flexibility and gives a farmer the power to control his environment to a greater degree than formerly.

The farm labor force

Much of our discussion of the farm labor force comes in Chapter 9 which deals with the social features of the structure of agriculture. But human labor is the main resource used on farms, and some attention must be directed to it at this point. As most of the farm labor supply (some four-fifths) is furnished by the farm operator and members of his family, payment for labor is now largely in terms of residual income after other operating costs are met. As such it includes returns to management. Hired labor is paid for as in other occupations. Because of the scattered employment, the lack of uniformity in employment conditions, and other reasons, hired agricultural labor has not been organized into unions as has industrial labor.

Wages and conditions of work for year-round farm workers in much of the country are influenced by farm incomes and living levels on the one hand and by industrial opportunities on the other. Troublesome economic and social questions arise in connection with migratory workers employed in cotton, fruit, and vegetable areas. Here employment is seasonal and intermittent. Technology and urban opportunities have reduced the demand for and the supply of such labor in recent years. But long-time trends in diets appear to be increasing the proportion of crops with high seasonal-labor requirements. Whether these trends will offset the reduced labor inputs resulting from improved technology remains to be seen.

Southern sharecroppers, who numbered 352,000 in 1950, are really hired workers paid in a share of the crop. About them more is said later.

Numbers of workers on farms have been declining for some years, as noted earlier. We now have around 9 million farm workers as compared with more than 13 million in 1910, according to AMS (Agriculture Marketing Service) estimates. The AMS estimates are on a slightly higher level than those reported in the census because they include some workers under 14 years of age, some whose major occupation lies off the farm, and some duplications. But the general trend shown is a true reflection. The separate series of estimates of man-hours worked on farms shows a similar downtrend since 1910.

Shifts in many service jobs from farms to a custom basis also mean that tasks formerly done by farm labor are now done to a greater extent by outside service agencies that are separate business firms. On the resource side one can think of implement dealers and service stations for cars, trucks, and tractors; trucking companies that transport farm produce to market on a fee basis; commercial feed, fertilizer, spraying, and liming companies that supply materials and services direct to the farm. The migratory seasonal labor that once moved with the wheat harvest in the Great Plains has largely disappeared, although there is a seasonal movement of combines with their attendant crews.

As we shall see in the next section, labor, though still the chief input in agriculture, does not occupy as large a place among the aggregate inputs as it did in 1910.

The capital goods complement

The capital goods complement of the triad of input resources, as noted earlier, comprises more than a third of the current inputs used in agricultural production. Interest, maintenance, and depreciation on buildings, machinery, and equipment; operation of motor vehicles and machinery; fertilizer, lime, and other miscellaneous items fall under this broad heading. Some of these inputs represent materials that are quickly used up in the processes of production; some are relatively durable and are consumed slowly over many years.

The changing configuration of the broad pattern of resource inputs from 1910 to 1950 is shown in table 3-4. Increases for capital items are evidently far greater than the 31-percent increase for land. In fact, an appreciable part of the increase for land during this period represents

TABLE 3-4.—PRODUCTION INPUTS IN UNITED STATES AGRICULTURE, INDEX NUMBERS, 1910 AND 1950 (1935–1939 = 100)

Inputs	1910	1950	Percentage 1950 of 1910
			Percent
Total inputs................	91	128	141
Labor [1]......................	107	85	79
Land [2].......................	83	109	131
Interest [3].....................	140	161	115
Taxes [4]......................	56	98	175
Depreciation [5]................	102	206	202
Operation of motor vehicles [6]....	1	282	28,200
Fertilizer and lime............	69	268	388
Miscellaneous items...........	76	118	155

[1] Total farm labor, including value of unpaid operator and family labor. Hence returns for management and for risk bearing are in this item.

[2] Net rent on land and buildings.

[3] Interest on investment in non-real-estate items, including horses and mules, motor vehicles, other machinery, crops, and livestock.

[4] Taxes on farm property. They can be considered payments for inputs provided by public authority, as for example, highways. Farm property taxes are also used to pay for public services, like schools, that are not properly farm inputs. On the other hand, other kinds of taxes are used to provide public services that *are* farm inputs. Therefore, property taxes may serve as a rough index of farm inputs from public services.

[5] Depreciation of buildings, motor vehicles, machinery, and equipment, including that fraction (currently 40 percent) of automobiles assigned to farm-business use.

[6] The enormous increase in machine power from 1910 to 1950 was accompanied by a decrease in farm-produced horse and mule power. This change is not directly revealed by these inputs, as the land and other inputs released were turned to other farm production.

Source: Unpublished data from Production Economics Research Branch, Agricultural Research Service. Actual quantities of inputs weighted by 1935–1939 prices.

capital improvements of land—buildings, fences, ditches, and drains. Kendrick and Jones's estimate of the increase in the physical quantity of intermediate products used in farm production indicated a level about four times as high in 1950 as in 1910.[3]

Power mechanization was the most startling change in this period. The item in table 3-4 on operation of motor vehicles reflects an important aspect of this shift. We have noted the long-time trends in numbers of horses and mules and tractors in fig. 1-2 and have indicated the release of land no longer needed for growing feed for horses and mules. An additional illustration of the changes in some of the principal farm machines in recent years is presented in fig. 3-2.

From 1941 to 1953, tractors and trucks doubled in number. Numbers of milking machines increased to a level three times, those of combines four times, and those of corn pickers five times as high as

[3] John W. Kendrick and Carl E. Jones, "Gross National Farm Product in Constant Dollars, 1910–1950," U. S. Dept. of Commerce, *Survey of Current Business*, Sept. 1951.

FIGURE 3-2. PRINCIPAL MACHINES ON FARMS, 1941 AND 1953

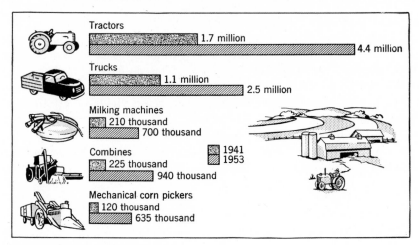

Tractors
1.7 million
4.4 million

Trucks
1.1 million
2.5 million

Milking machines
210 thousand
700 thousand

Combines
225 thousand
940 thousand
1941
1953

Mechanical corn pickers
120 thousand
635 thousand

Source: Agricultural Research Service.

prewar. Aggregate increases in all farm machinery and power as measured from 1935–1939 totaled 76 percent.

Changes in many farm inputs are difficult to show because of their
variety and their shifting characteristics. A few outstanding items
were brought together in fig. 3-3 to show something of their range.

FIGURE 3-3. CHANGES IN FARM INPUTS; 1952 COMPARED WITH 1935–39

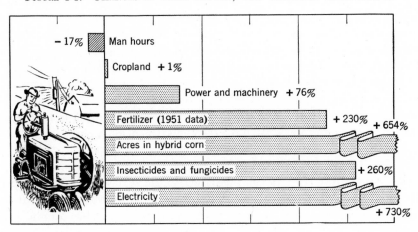

− 17% Man hours
Cropland + 1%
Power and machinery + 76%
Fertilizer (1951 data) + 230%
Acres in hybrid corn + 654%
Insecticides and fungicides + 260%
Electricity + 730%

Source: Agricultural Research Service.

Greater and more widespread use of commercial fertilizer is a significant item. Fertilizer also offers promise of further expansion with
important effects on yield for a number of crops. Hybrid seed corn is

an example of a development that may be repeated with other seeds in the future. Insecticides and fungicides are often very effective, and the increased knowledge concerning them has led to wider use. Development of power and machinery for effective application of such control measures illustrates the interrelationship that exists between many parallel technical developments. The positive aid of friendly insects illustrates another phase of applied technology. Heavy stocking with bees as pollinators is done to increase yields of alfalfa seed and of many fruits.

Control of weeds by chemicals is a recent innovation that may solve difficult cultural and labor problems for some crops. Field spraying for small grains, sugar beets, and cotton is a hopeful measure in certain areas.

Technology—the unseen force

Classical economists held that the invisible forces of competition would cause economic affairs to work out for the best. Their explanation has been shown to be greatly oversimplified even for their own day, but if they could see some of the marvels of present technology they might describe the dynamics of technology as the unseen force that apparently directs our affairs.

Chemical and biological discoveries have enabled us to do things in laboratories and on farms that have greatly increased control of natural forces at little additional cost. Hybrid seed corn, for example, adds but little to the cash cost per acre of growing corn, yet the effect has been to raise yields of corn about 20 percent.

New technology, whether mechanical, genetic, chemical, social, or other, does not spring full bloom into being. Some of it comes from farm practice as farmers go about their daily routines, some is borrowed from industrial experience. But, as mentioned previously, the greater part is a result of publicly supported research and extension programs carried on by the States and the Federal Government in the Land-Grant College system and the United States Department of Agriculture.

The farm land inventory [4]

A review of the relative roles assigned to the several broad categories of resources used in agriculture thus brings us to further consideration of land. We conclude that its relative significance has diminished considerably and may diminish still more. This is the inevitable outcome of successful application of improved technology and more capital goods to agriculture. Our ties with the soil become more flexible

---

[4] For a detailed inventory of land used for agriculture in the United States, see H. H. Wooten, "Major Uses of Land in the United States," *U. S. Dept. Agr. Tech. Bul. 1082*, Oct. 1953.

and less rigid.   In the Western World the fear of Malthusianism recedes into the background.

But we should not underestimate the importance of understanding and appraising land resources because of this apparent reversal in the relative position of land and capital goods.   We can no longer bring so large a part of the resources used in agriculture under the land canopy.   But those "original and indestructible properties" that loomed so large in the thinking of the early economists are still present.   The great variety and wide spatial sweep of lands and soils set agriculture apart from other kinds of activity and have much to do with determining the general pattern of farm production.

Let us look for a moment at the map in fig. 3-4, which shows the relative place of cultivated land in the world and in the United States. Only about 8 percent of the total land surface of the globe is cultivated land, and most of that is in the temperate zones (fig. 3-4).   Observe the irregular distribution over the several continents.

Nearly a fifth of the world's cultivated land lies within our own country, although we have less than a tenth of the earth's land surface. The circumstances of geological development, the distribution and orientation of mountain chains and drainage systems, and all the matters of physical geography and climate have combined to give this result.

Within continental United States are some 3 million square miles of land surface, or nearly 2 billion acres.   The first broad picture to be visualized is the distribution of total land areas between agricultural and nonagricultural uses.   In terms of percentages and based on the Census of 1950, the tabulated relationships appear:

	Percent
Census farms	61
Grazing lands not in farms	21
Land not used for farming	18
Total land area	100

This means that more than four-fifths of the surface of the United States serves some agricultural use, although only about three-fifths lies within individual farm boundaries.   Nearly three-fourths of the grazing lands not in farms are publicly owned.   The productivity of grazing lands not in farms is much lower than that of lands within farms because of the character of the soil, lack of rainfall, inclusion of rough terrain, and multiple use for forests, recreation, and other purposes.   In 1949, publicly owned grazing land produced only 5.4 percent of our forage requirements.[5]   This quantity of forage is valuable for cattle

---

[5] R. D. Davidson, "Federal and State Rural Lands, 1950," *U. S. Dept. Agr. Circ. 909*, May 1952, p. 67.

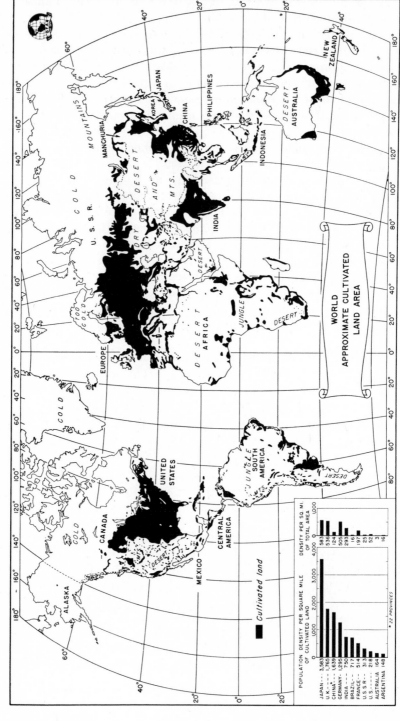

FIGURE 3-4. WORLD APPROXIMATE CULTIVATED LAND AREA

Source: Foreign Agricultural Service.

and sheep in the areas affected, but it is still a small part of our total feed resources.

In passing it is well to note this statement: "It has been estimated (1949) that the present grazing capacity of the Federal range lands is less than half of its original capacity. This decline has been attributed largely to overgrazing and inadequate maintenance." [6] State-owned lands and privately owned range outside of farms may have fared better because of location. Management of range lands has improved in recent years, and it is believed that further possible improvements could increase grazing capacity.

It should be noted that, although grazing lands not in farms are not included in the census of farms, production of cattle and sheep that grazed on these lands is reflected in census data, because the animals are owned by farm and ranch operators who report from their head-quarters units.

Multiple use of land complicates the task of classifying lands. The following classification according to major land use gives a different impression from the preceding one:

Major use of land	Percent
Cropland	21
Pasture and grazing land, nonforested	37
Forest and woodland grazed	17
Forest and woodland not grazed	15
Special uses	6
Miscellaneous other	4
Total land area	100

The relative contribution of cropland to total agricultural production is much greater than its share of the total land area might suggest. Although cropland occupies only a third as much land as pasture and grazing land, it produces more than two-thirds of the feed nutrients consumed by livestock. In addition, it produces food crops for direct human consumption and nonfood crops like cotton, tobacco, and vegetable oils. All told, cropland furnishes the land base for around 90 percent of the value of total agricultural output.

Areas of *special uses* include farmsteads, feedlots, lanes, ditches, roads, highways, urban areas, industrial sites, parks and other special-use areas. *Miscellaneous* other areas include barren land, rock and open marsh, sand dunes, and desert. Obviously more than half of the forest and woodland can be used for grazing.

Special-use areas need to be considered separately if their significance is to be understood. These areas were classified into the separate categories shown in table 3-5.

---

6 Davidson, *ibid.*, p. 38.

TABLE 3-5.—SPECIAL-USE AREAS, UNITED STATES, 1950

Areas	Million acres
Urban areas [1]	18
Rural highways and railways	23
Farmsteads	10
Parks	19
Wildlife areas	9
National defense	21
Other services	5
Total special-use areas	105

[1] All towns and cities having 1,000 or more people, including both incorporated and unincorporated places.

Source: U. S. Dept. of Agriculture, "Supplement to Major Uses of Land in the United States," *U. S. Dept. Agr. Tech. Bul. 108.2*, Sept. 1953, p. 36.

In view of the high degree of urbanization of our economy, it is astonishing to note that the strictly urban areas cover a little less than 1 percent of our land surface. Even adding in all the rural highways and railways outside the cities makes the total only slightly more than 2 percent. Farmsteads alone occupy more than half as much space as all urban areas.

Open country is the dominant feature of the American landscape. A traveler from another planet who surveyed the continent from outer space would probably consider us an agricultural or pastoral people, unless he observed certain signs that indicate the presence of large industrial works.

Since 1880, notable shifts have taken place in the use of land (fig. 3-5). Total acreage of land in farms, crops, and pastures has increased. This has occurred mainly in the West; in many parts of the East the acreage of land in farms has decreased.

The physical layout. The land relief map of the United States in fig. 3-6 indicates the broad divisions of the country between the rough, mountainous regions and the smoother plains and valleys. Description of the surface features and their climatic connections often starts with the North-South line marked by the one-hundredth meridian, which passes through North Dakota, South Dakota, Nebraska, Kansas, Oklahoma, and Texas. East of this meridian are the lower, more humid areas, and west of it lie the higher, dryer lands, which have less agriculture per square mile. Still farther west in the Pacific Coast States are areas of high rainfall and intensive agriculture.

One needs to compare the relief map with maps for rainfall and temperature to understand the principal climatic factors that affect agriculture in different regions (figs. 3-7 and 3-8). Latitude and elevation are related to both rainfall and temperature in obvious ways. The particular crops and combinations of crops that can be grown have definite physical limitations. Some of these limitations are absolute; some are relative. Citrus fruits, for example, are closely restricted by temperatures to certain southern areas. Other crops, like grains, can be grown over a wide range, but with quite different yields. Special soil preferences affect crops like tobacco and orchard fruits more than

FIGURE 3-5. TREND IN LAND UTILIZATION, 1880 TO 1950

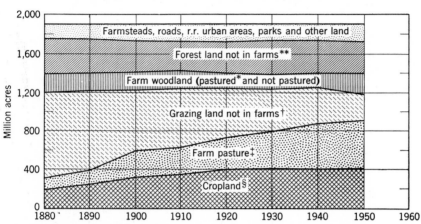

** Chiefly commercial timber land; approximately 120 million acres were estimated grazed during the years 1949 to 1951.
* 135 million acres were reported grazed in 1949.
† Includes grassland, arid woodland, and brushland grazed.
‡ Open pasture in farms, including cropland used only for pasture and other plowable pasture.
§ Includes soil improvement crops, summer fallow, and land seeded to crops for harvest the succeeding year. Cropland acreages are for the year preceding the date of the census.
Source: Agricultural Research Service.

others. The comparative advantage of crops and of livestock depends upon their adaptability to many physical and climatic conditions.

Economic factors. The physical layout of resources is like a great natural stage upon which the moving play of economic life takes place. As in any theater, the characteristics of the stage set bounds within which the action is circumscribed. These basic limitations affect the comparative advantage of particular kinds of farm production. But within the broad confines of the fixed resources, many modifications are possible. Stage properties (the capital equipment) may be replaced, actors may come and go, the plot may be rewritten, the audience may change, the very nature of the production may be revolutionized. The natural features and the physical layout of the United States have been much the same since pre-Columbian times. But the economic stage setting has changed greatly. Agricultural systems prevalent under the Indian tribes led to one pattern of agriculture. Colonists of

FIGURE 3-6. LAND RELIEF OF THE UNITED STATES

Source: Agricultural Research Service.

Figure 3-7. Average Annual Precipitation

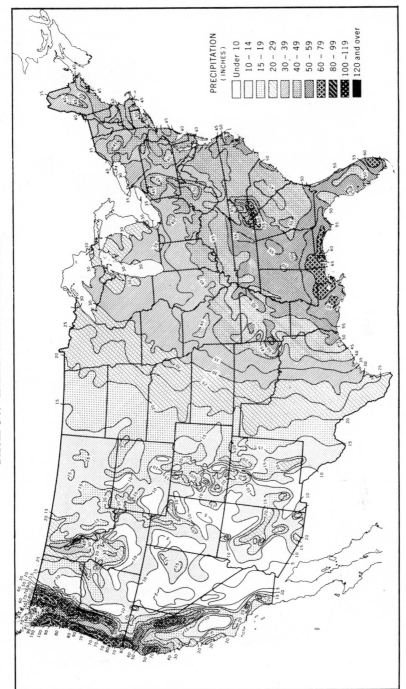

Source: Weather Bureau.

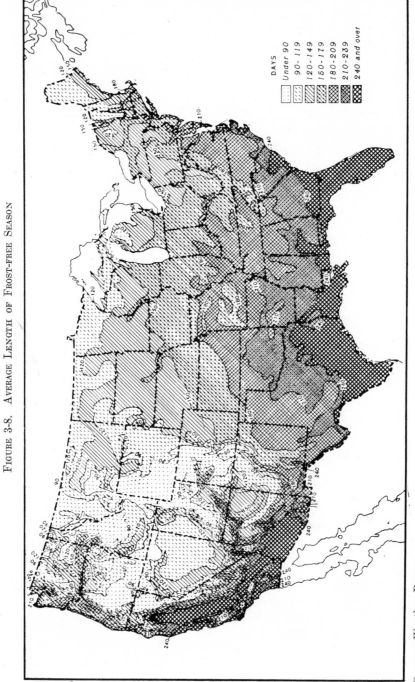

FIGURE 3-8. AVERAGE LENGTH OF FROST-FREE SEASON

Source: Weather Bureau.

European origin introduced institutions and practices that led to pronounced changes and to differences between colonies. The Spanish, the Dutch, the French, the English, and others proceeded to farm in the New World in their different ways. Traces of these differences still survive. The westward march of settlement, the growth of population, the unfolding technology of the last century were reflected in continuous changes in types of farming.

Another way of explaining part of the relationship between physical and economic determinants of types of farming is contained in the location theory advanced by the German economist Von Thünen in his three-volume lifetime work *The Isolated State,* which was written from 1826 to 1863. With his orderly German mind, which tended to select the forces most susceptible to geometric arrangement, Von Thünen imagined an isolated city-state surrounded by an immense level plain on which there was complete uniformity of natural conditions. In this way he eliminated all physical differences in the natural environment except one—distance from market. He then worked out the pattern of agricultural production that would evolve in terms of concentric zones that would minimize transportation costs. Bulky, perishable products like milk and vegetables would be grown in inner zones near the market. More concentrated products like beef and butter would be produced in the outer zones. This simplified explanation focused attention on the significance of economic forces in developing types of farming.

Man's continuing efforts to adjust to the circumstances of his environment is the key to an understanding of the forces responsible for the major types of farming. Most of our discussion of types of farms is deferred to Chapter 5, but the broad regional pattern is explained here.

Major type-of-farming regions. Economists explain how major type-of-farming regions develop in terms of the broad Principle of Comparative Advantage.[7] This is a relatively simple concept, which at times becomes rather intricate in its application. But, in general, it means that individuals and areas tend to produce the things that pay best under prevailing conditions and circumstances. The main determinants of the geographic pattern of production and the combinations that are reported in the broad type-of-farming regions shown in fig. 3-9 are the natural and economic factors just mentioned.

The general regions indicated on this map are familiar to most of us. The Corn Belt, the Cotton Belt, the Northern Dairy Region, Great Plains Wheat and Small Grains, Western Range Livestock, Tobacco and General Farming, and Fruit, Truck, and Special Crops, are well

---

7 See the development of this principle in Ronald L. Mighell and John D. Black, *Interregional Competition in Agriculture,* Harvard University Press, Cambridge, 1951.

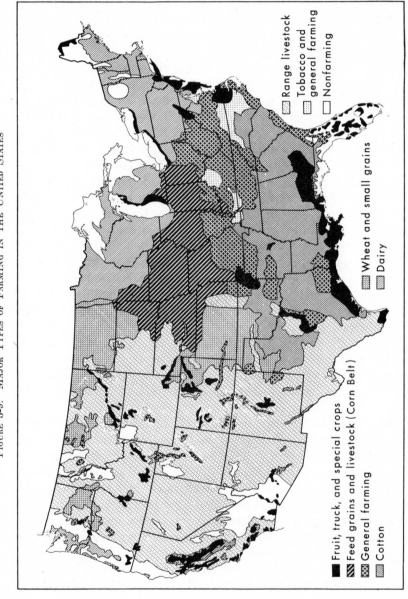

FIGURE 3-9.   MAJOR TYPES OF FARMING IN THE UNITED STATES

Range livestock

Tobacco and general farming

Nonfarming

Wheat and small grains

Dairy

Fruit, truck, and special crops

Feed grains and livestock (Corn Belt)

General farming

Cotton

Source: Agricultural Research Service.

known, and for the most part they have been about where they are for several decades. Some rather significant changes have taken place, but the vivid outlines are plain. These outlines trace back to the whole underlying complex; those permanent and "indestructible" natural characteristics of the land, the soil, and the climate.

If we take time to look at a few selected maps for individual classes of crops and livestock, we shall see better how things work out. Crops are more closely related to soils and climate than are livestock. Some

FIGURE 3-10. COTTON HARVESTED, ACREAGE, 1949

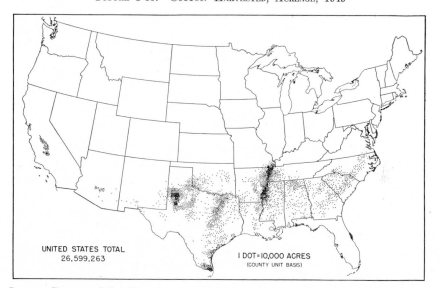

UNITED STATES TOTAL
26,599,263

I DOT=10,000 ACRES
(COUNTY UNIT BASIS)

Source: Bureau of the Census.

crops, such as cotton, tobacco, and peanuts, are rather closely restricted to certain areas (figs. 3-10 and 3-11).

Notice in fig. 3-10 how the acreage of cotton is confined to a definite belt of Southern States and also how greater concentrations occur in certain areas within the belt. Temperature and length of growing season place a northern limit on production of cotton. Soil and surface conditions play the greatest part in determining areas of concentration. Especially since the partial mechanization of cotton production, the center of gravity has shifted westward. In the far west, irrigation is important. This explains the location of cotton acreage in California, Arizona, and New Mexico.

Tobacco appears to be strongly influenced by soil preferences. The dot map shows the relative concentration of tobacco, but it does not fully reveal the still greater concentration of each of the several types of tobacco.

Let us look at two additional examples of concentrated areas of production: potatoes and vegetables harvested for sale (figs. 3-12 and 3-13).

The potato map (1949 map, fig. 3-12) shows a high degree of concentration in a relatively small number of areas. This was not always true; potatoes were once grown much more widely (1899 map, fig. 3-12). Technology, in terms of a combination of mechanization, disease con-

FIGURE 3-11. TOBACCO HARVESTED, ACREAGE, 1949

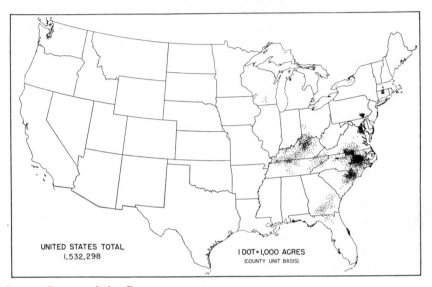

UNITED STATES TOTAL
1,532,298

I DOT = 1,000 ACRES
(COUNTY UNIT BASIS)

Source: Bureau of the Census.

trol, seed selection, fertilizer—a collection of improved practices—brought about this particular situation. In this instance technology probably permitted concentration on the best natural sites.

The map on vegetables harvested for sale reflects a similar specialization. The dots stand out less sharply here, but this is only because a considerable number of different vegetables are combined in a composite total. Even so, the areas are quite ·distinct.

The maps for corn and wheat illustrate a more diffused distribution with greater densities in certain regions (figs. 3-14 and 3-15). These great food and feed crops can be grown almost anywhere in the United States. They are widely grown, but the main centers of production are well marked. The greater part of the wheat is found in the Great Plains States, and most of the corn is in the Corn Belt.

Livestock enterprises are less closely confined to particular areas, at least less so now than formerly. Still, the reduction in shipping

FIGURE 3-12. IRISH POTATOES, ACREAGE, 1899 (TOP) AND 1949 (BOTTOM)

[Acreage shown on bottom map excludes acres for farms with less than 15 bushels harvested]

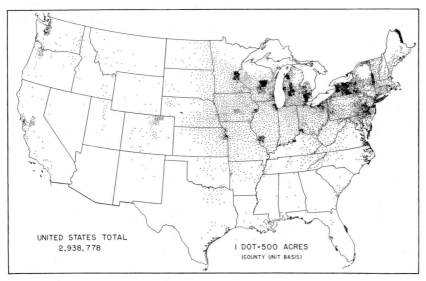

UNITED STATES TOTAL
2,938,778

I DOT=500 ACRES
(COUNTY UNIT BASIS)

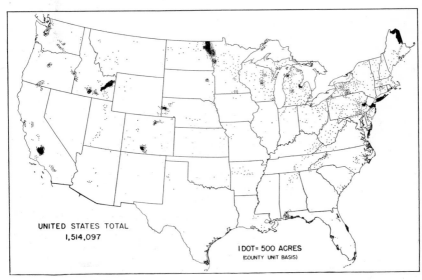

UNITED STATES TOTAL
1,514,097

I DOT= 500 ACRES
(COUNTY UNIT BASIS)

Source: Bureau of the Census.

FIGURE 3-13. VEGETABLES (OTHER THAN IRISH AND SWEET POTATOES) HARVESTED
FOR SALE, ACREAGE, 1949

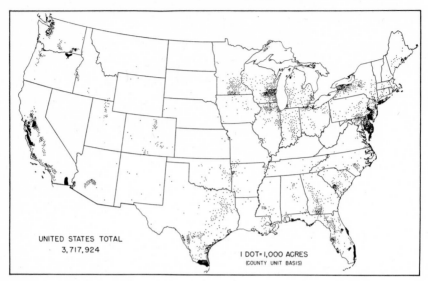

UNITED STATES TOTAL
3,717,924

I DOT= 1,000 ACRES
(COUNTY UNIT BASIS)

Source: Bureau of the Census.

FIGURE 3-14. CORN HARVESTED FOR GRAIN, ACREAGE, 1949

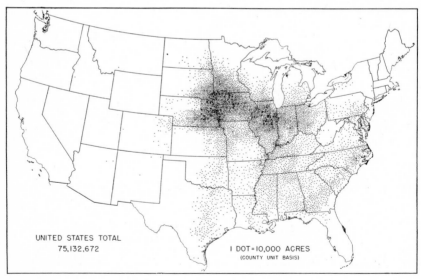

UNITED STATES TOTAL
75,132,672

I DOT=10,000 ACRES
(COUNTY UNIT BASIS)

Source: Bureau of the Census.

FIGURE 3-15. ALL WHEAT THRESHED, ACREAGE, 1949

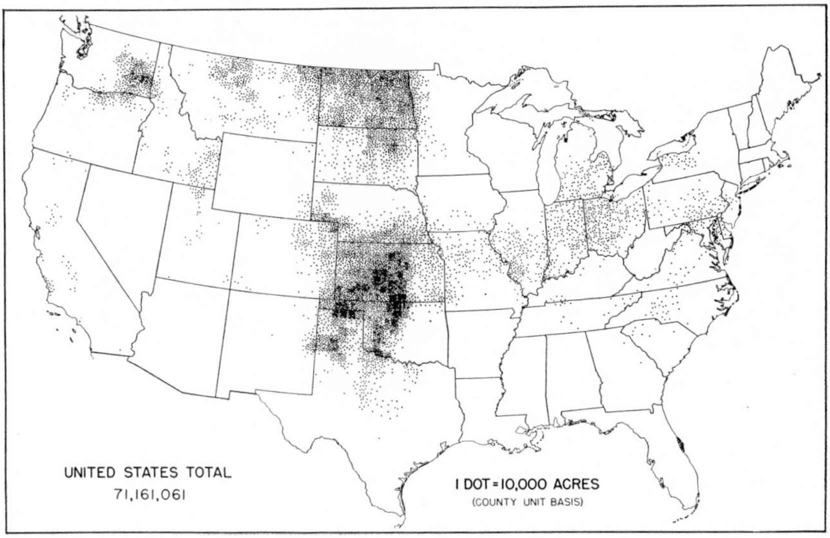

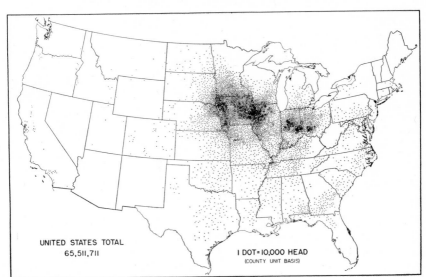

Source: Bureau of the Census.

FIGURE 3-16. HOGS AND PIGS SOLD ALIVE, NUMBER, 1949

Source: Bureau of the Census.

FIGURE 3-17. MILK COWS, NUMBER, APRIL 1, 1950

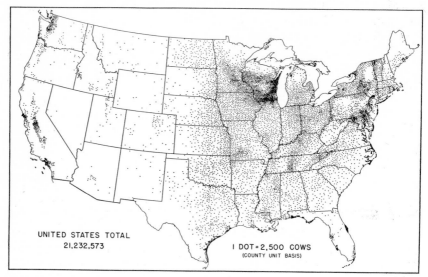

UNITED STATES TOTAL
21,232,573

1 DOT = 2,500 COWS
(COUNTY UNIT BASIS)

Source: Bureau of the Census.

FIGURE 3-18. CHICKENS SOLD, NUMBER, 1949

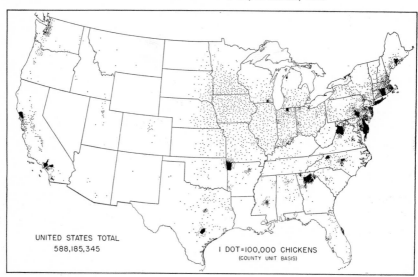

UNITED STATES TOTAL
588,185,345

1 DOT = 100,000 CHICKENS
(COUNTY UNIT BASIS)

Source: Bureau of the Census.

weight achieved by converting feeds to livestock products keeps much livestock production near the source of feed supplies. One can see how closely hog production is connected with corn production by comparing the hog map with the corn map (fig. 3-16).

Dairy production furnishes perhaps the best example of a widely diffused livestock enterprise, but it is especially concentrated in the Northeast and the Lake States, where pasture and hay conditions are more favorable than elsewhere (fig. 3-17). A considerable part of the concentrate feeds used, especially in the Northeast, are shipped in from surplus-grain-producing areas. With the declining demand for butterfat and the rising demand for fluid milk and nonfat solids, there has been a tendency for greater market orientation in recent years. Fluid milk is relatively bulky and has a high transportation cost.

Production of chickens and eggs has also been widely diffused. Technology has made some striking changes in this picture, especially in production of poultry meat (fig. 3-18). The map of chickens sold shows how well-marked the areas of broiler production have become.

Thus, the explanation of type-of-farming regions in general terms traces back to broad physical and economic conditions. The location of physical resources determines many of the boundaries on the map, but the place of technology and capital goods becomes important in shifting the scenery upon the stage. The land base remains fundamental, but command over more capital goods, and over technology, has made agriculture more flexible and subject to control. Man is no longer governed by the blind forces of nature. He has learned to harness and guide them in many directions.

CHAPTER 4

STRUCTURE OF COMMERCIAL FARMS—SCALE

Up to this point we have looked at the structure of agriculture pretty much from the outside and in terms of aggregate dimensions. A sensitive air-borne camera, equipped with appropriate computing devices, might be able to picture most of this outer structure. But it would not be able to pierce the surface and reveal how resources are actually organized for production. Nor would it be able to perceive the mechanism by which the decisions are made that put productive activities in motion and keep them in the proper channels.

To record the inner structure of agriculture, to describe key production units and their makeup, analytical tools more akin to the high-powered microscope and the X-ray are needed. The moment we turn our imaginary structural microscope on agriculture, we become aware of the myriads of operating units, or "farms." Altogether the census counted 5.4 million farms in the United States in 1950. What are these farms? Why are there so many? What do they stand for in the total economy? No short answers will suffice for these questions. But we can say that farms represent a persistent stronghold of the forces of competition.

Farms are the active business firms, the radiant points of competitive energy that make the plans, focus the decisions, and carry on the work of agriculture. Farms and farmers are sometimes spoken of as though they can be considered independently. But reflection will show this to be a fallacy. In this discussion, we may sometimes conveniently center on one or the other, but we must keep in mind their fundamental unity.

Examination of the census definition of a farm reveals a working compromise between the practical problems of census enumeration and the economic concept of the business firm. To begin with a census farm is an operating unit, not an ownership unit. Every census farm is a "place" with a "farm operator."

The 1950 Census states: "A farm operator is a person who operates a farm either performing the work himself or directly supervising it. He may be an owner, a hired manager, or a tenant, renter, or sharecropper. . . . The number of farm operators is considered the same as the number of farms."

Farms counted in the 1950 Census of Agriculture include all places of 3 acres or more that *produced* $150 or more of farm products in 1949 (exclusive of home gardens) and all places of less than 3 acres that *sold* at least $150 worth of farm products. In addition, other places that would normally meet these criteria were counted. Most of the 5.4 million census farms are also economic "firms." But about 350,000 cropper units were counted as farms in the 1950 Census, and these are not true "firms." Nor are all the noncommercial farms "firms." And a very small but unknown number of census farms under certain forms of corporate control might not qualify in the strict economic sense. As we shall see later, a separate analysis was made to corral the cropper units. This analysis was presented in a special report on multiple-unit operations.[1] In the multiple-unit report, satellite cropper units are combined with their respective "home farms" to show the true operating firms.

Farms by scale of operation

The 5.4 million farms counted in 1950 cover a very wide range of economic conditions, types of farming, systems of production, and associated economic and social problems. People may speak of an average farm, but the term "average" covers a combination of such widely varying conditions that it is likely to prove meaningless or even misleading. The difficulty of using an average that covers widely differing conditions may be illustrated by automobile traffic. The average density of traffic on U. S. Highway Number 1 between Washington, D. C., and New York City may not seem excessive. Yet we know from the accidents that occur that it is one of the most dangerously crowded highways in the country. It is not the average but the densities at certain times and places that are critical. Until we classify the highway data by time and by segments of this highway, it is not possible to picture truly the traffic situations with which we must cope.

So it is with data on farms. The first step in the process is to separate all farms into the 3.7 million commercial farms and the 1.7 million noncommercial farms. Commercial farms are those primarily concerned with farming, and noncommercial farms include part-time, residential, and other unusual farms not operated for commercial profit.[2] Noncommercial farms produce only about 2.5 percent of the farm products sold, and, as their problems are mainly nonagricultural, it is helpful to set them apart for separate consideration. Failure to make this separation and lack of understanding of the many small part-time

---

1 Bureau of the Census, *Multiple-Unit Operations, U. S. Census of Agriculture: 1950*, Vol. 5, *Special Reports*, Part 2, 1952.

2 The 1950 Census of Agriculture designates "noncommercial farms" as "other farms," and the "unusual noncommercial farms" are called "abnormal farms." The terms "noncommercial" and "unusual" are more appropriate and are used in this book.

FIGURE 4-1. NUMBER OF COMMERCIAL FARMS AND VALUE OF FARM PRODUCTS SOLD
FROM COMMERCIAL FARMS, BY SIZE OF OPERATION, UNITED STATES, 1949

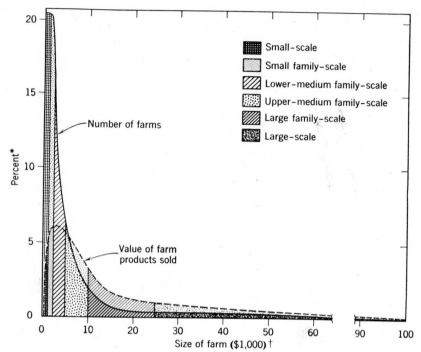

* Percentage of total number of commercial farms and of total sales of farm products per $1,000-
size interval.

† Economic size in terms of value of sales of farm products.

Source: Data are from Bureau of the Census.

and residential farms included in the total census enumeration often
give rise to serious misconceptions. Over-all data on characteristics
of farms include these noncommercial farms and as they make up 30
percent of the numbers of all farms, their inclusion produces a diminished picture of the average farm which is unrealistic if one is thinking
of commercial farms. Grouping separately avoids this difficulty.

The 3.7 million commercial farms are by definition all those farms
with a value of sales of farm products of $1,200 or more, and in addi-
tion all those with sales of $250 to $1,199, provided the operator worked
off the farm less than 100 days and if the income of himself and members of his family from nonfarm sources was less than the total value of
all farm products sold.

The next step in the classification process is to become familiar with
the distribution of commercial farms by scale of operation. Size in
acres is the time-honored method of gauging scale in agriculture. But
this method, although it is useful for a given area or for similar types

of farming, has shortcomings for general use. The increasing complexity of farming makes it important to choose other yardsticks. Value of sales of farm products is one measure that has been developed for this purpose.

Figure 4-1 presents two basic pictures that should be retained as mental images of total numbers of farms by size of operation and of total value of farm products sold by size of operation. Three significant characteristics that are common to both distributions should be remembered. First, they are smooth continuous distributions with no natural boundary markers. Nowhere can it be said that one size begins or that another one ends. Second, there is an immense range in size. Third, both distributions are skewed, with a tail running far to the right. There are many farms in the small sizes and relatively few in the large sizes, with a long tapering-out toward the upper end. One difference between the two distributions should be kept in mind. That is that the proportion of total sales in the upper size groups is much greater than the proportion of farms.

We will need to have these two basic pictures in mind. In setting up economic classes of commercial farms for detailed analysis, a simple statistical device of varying the size of class intervals was used to compress the long tapering tail of each distribution into a more easily manageable shape. This is good statistical practice, even though it may resemble an Indian rope trick. But for those who do not remind themselves that they are looking through a statistician's stereoscope, it produces a distortion that covers up some significant features of the agricultural landscape.

Commercial farms were classified by the 1950 Census of Agriculture into the tabulated economic classes in accordance with value of sales.[3]

	Sales of farm products
Class I, Large-scale	$25,000 or more
Class II, Large family-scale	10,000 to 24,999
Class III, Upper-medium family-scale	5,000 to 9,999
Class IV, Lower-medium family-scale	2,500 to 4,999
Class V, Small family-scale	1,200 to 2,499
Class VI, Small-scale	[1] 250 to 1,199

[1] Provided there are less than 100 days off-farm work by the operator and that income of operator and his family from nonfarm sources is less than the value of all farm products sold.

After class VI, the width of the class intervals approximately doubles from one class to the next higher. The class interval for small-scale

[3] The 1950 Census of Agriculture designates "economic classes" by class numbers only. Production economists in the Agricultural Research Service devised the scale names, in order to have descriptive labels for economic classes. In this book both sets of terms are used interchangeably. It must be recognized that value of sales of farm products in a single year is an imperfect gauge of scale. If a measure of total inputs were available, it would be more accurate. A similar size classification by economic classes was first developed in the 1945 Census. See for example Kenneth L. Bachman and Ronald W. Jones, "Sizes of Farms in the United States," U. S. Dept. Agr. Tech. Bul. 1019, July 1950.

farms, for example, is $950, whereas that for large family-scale farms is $15,000, or about 16 times as great. The effects of this accordionlike compression of the frequency distribution can be observed in the accompanying tabulation showing numbers of farms in each economic size

	Thousand farms
Large-scale....................	103
Large family-scale.............	381
Upper-medium family-scale.....	721
Lower-medium family-scale.....	882
Small family-scale.............	902
Small-scale....................	717
All commercial..............	3,706

class. For example, numbers of small family-scale and lower-medium family-scale farms are nearly the same, but for lower-medium family-scale farms one must go twice as far along the size axis to find this number.

Under this classification more than three-fourths of the commercial farms are classed within the family-scale groups. Less than 3 percent are large-scale, and nearly 20 percent are small-scale.

In order to keep things in perspective, it may be useful to apply another graphic yardstick. The difference in average size between small-scale and large-scale farms, as measured by value of farm sales, is of the same order as that between a 1-story and a 75-story office building. Keep in mind that this is only the range between the average sizes in each class. The extreme range from the smallest to the largest individual commercial farm is not known exactly, because the census does not reveal the identity of individual farms. But it is safe to say that there are a few unusually large ranches or giant corporation farms that could be rated as equivalent to 500-story office buildings on this architectural measuring rod.

Part-time and residential farms taken together are about like half-story buildings. The range from small family-scale to large family-scale farms is like that between a 2½-story building and a 20-story building.

Scale of operations in agriculture contrasts sharply with that found in other major industry groups. Business firms in other lines are distributed in a storied range of the same general shape, but the average height of the range (the size of the firm) is much greater and the number of firms is smaller. In 1950, the average manufacturing firm was 33 times as large as the average farm, in terms of income per enterprise (table 4-1). Even in retail trade, in which small enterprises are more numerous, the average firm was 3 times as large as in agriculture.

A significant part of the industrial world is organized into large corporate bodies, which operate huge physical plants that employ thousands of people. Some 4.6 million people, about a third of all

TABLE 4-1.—AVERAGE NUMBER OF BUSINESS FIRMS IN OPERATION, INCOME BEFORE FEDERAL AND STATE INCOME AND EXCESS PROFIT TAXES, AND INCOME PER ENTERPRISE, BY MAJOR INDUSTRY GROUPS, UNITED STATES, 1950

(Includes both incorporated and unincorporated businesses)

Industry	Number of firms	Income before taxes	Income per enterprise
	Thousands	*Million dollars*	*Dollars*
Mining and quarrying.............	34	1,672	49,176
Contract construction............	358	4,215	11,774
Manufacturing..................	303	25,194	83,149
Transportation, communication, and other public utilities........	194	4,743	24,449
Wholesale trade.................	204	3,565	17,476
Retail trade.....................	1,685	13,220	7,846
Finance, insurance, and real estate.	347	3,957	11,404
Service industries................	854	7,180	8,408
Agriculture.....................	5,382	13,567	2,521

Source: Bureau of the Census, *Statistical Abstract of the United States: 1953*, pp. 478, 483.

employees in manufacturing in 1950, were employed by concerns with more than 1,000 employees (table 4-2). These concerns made up fewer than 1 percent of the manufacturing establishments, but they accounted for 36 percent of the value added in manufacturing in 1950.

Thus a few large luminaries frequently dominate an entire sector of an industry, with perhaps some lesser satellites, in which the embers of

TABLE 4-2.—NUMBER AND PERCENTAGE OF MANUFACTURING ESTABLISHMENTS, VALUE ADDED BY MANUFACTURE, AND NUMBER OF EMPLOYEES, BY SIZE CLASS, UNITED STATES, 1950

Size class	Number of establishments	Value added by manufacture	Number of employees	Percentage of total		
				Number of establishments	Value added by manufacture	Number of employees
	Thousands	*Million dollars*	*Thousands*			
All establishments.........	247.3	89,676	14,370	100.0	100.0	100.0
1 to 249 employees...........	236.9	32,167	5,896	95.9	35.9	41.0
250 to 499 employees.........	5.8	12,432	2,009	2.3	13.9	14.0
500 to 999 employees.........	2.7	12,308	1,868	1.1	13.7	13.0
1,000 to 2,499 employees......	1.4	14,604	2,063	0.5	16.3	14.4
2,500 and over employees.....	0.5	18,165	2,534	0.2	20.2	17.6

Source: Bureau of the Census, *Annual Survey of Manufactures: 1949–1950*, p. 116.

the fires of competition may still glow softly, held firmly in restricted orbits. Not so in most of agriculture, in which the radiant points of competitive energy still number millions and are widely spread over the indicated range in size.

Trends in numbers of farms by economic classes

A view of the unfolding structure of agriculture in the United States must include an examination of trends in numbers of farms by economic classes. Even an approximate appraisal will help to avoid some of the misinterpretations that plague those who fail to separate commercial farms from other farms and who are unaware that their trends have been in opposite directions.

Within commercial farms the tracing of trends for separate economic classes faces complex statistical problems in adjusting for changing price levels, increasing productivity, and the like. Ingenious procedures for meeting some of these difficulties have been devised.[4] Before looking at the trends themselves, we should consider the meaning of the terms in which scale is to be measured and the procedure used. This is one of those not infrequent situations in which an appreciation of the concepts is almost imperative to clear understanding. These concepts are not difficult, but they are subject to confusion.

For our purpose the most meaningful concept of scale is in terms of constant man-equivalents with other resources varying. This puts the measure of scale squarely in terms of what a man (plus his changing knowledge and capital equipment) can accomplish per unit of time. It means that with improving technology and increasing investment per man, the average size of farm in acres, equipment, and other inputs must expand at the same rate as output per man-hour if it is to stay in the same scale class. This may seem a little like the Queen's explanation to Alice in *Through the Looking Glass,* "Now *here,* you see, it takes all the running *you* can do, to keep in the same place." But it makes sense if we think of scale in terms of a one-man, two-man, or family-scale farm. If these farms are to stay in the same size class, they must necessarily change as technology and investment change. A two-man farm will be larger in terms of resources and outputs, but it is still a two-man operation.[5]

Two principal statistical operations on economic-class (farm-sales) data are necessary in order to measure trends in scale as we define it.

4 Kenneth L. Bachman, "Changes in Scale in Commercial Farming and Their Implications," *Journal of Farm Economics,* May 1952, pp. 157–172; Jackson V. McElveen and Kenneth L. Bachman, "Low Production Farms," *U. S. Dept. Agr. Inf. Bul. 108,* June 1953.

5 The measure of scale over time is frequently a relative one; this is true in many fields. For example, in the case of popular makes of automobiles, what we call a small car—a Ford, Chevrolet, or a Plymouth—is as large as many large cars were a generation ago. But, a large house of today would have been regarded as a small house in 1900 when families were larger.

The first is to correct for changes in the price level; the second is to adjust for changes in productivity.

Briefly, the method starts with the 1950 separation and works back through earlier census years, trying to apply similar criteria for value of products and output per man-hour to determine economic class limits or boundaries. Values of products are brought into line with the 1950 price level by adjusting values of earlier years by the AMS (Agricultural Marketing Service) farm price index. Correction for productivity similarly is made by adjusting earlier years by the ARS (Agricultural Research Service) index of output per man-hour.

This procedure assumes that boundaries between economic classes in each census cross section are as nearly as possible like those of 1950, after adjusting for changes in price levels and changes in productivity per man-hour. In the absence of more detailed information, the same relative changes in productivity per man-hour are assumed for all size classes.

The reason for the adjustment in the price level is obvious, although some questions may remain about such matters as the point of cutoff between enumerated and nonenumerated rural residences. But the adjustment in productivity is more subtle. By this adjustment we have developed a unit of scale (size) that will expand with increases in the average farmer's accomplishment per unit of time whether these increases are due to improved technology or simply to greater capital investment. Unit of scale expands with rate of accomplishment per man, plus his increasing complement of capital goods and technology.

Estimates made in this way show that from 1930 to 1950 numbers of commercial farms dropped 30 percent (table 4-3). This rate of decrease was more than twice as great as that for all farms. The other side of the coin is the even more rapid rate of increase for part-time and residential farms. The smaller base for part-time and residential farms meant that the absolute numbers involved were only enough to offset part of the decline in commercial farms. Part-time and residential farms are estimated to have increased from 1.0 million in 1930 to nearly 1.7 million in 1950.

Changes within the three broad subgroups of commercial farms are also significant (table 4-4). Numbers of family-scale farms have decreased most, a full third from 1930. Numbers of large-scale farms have dropped 20 percent, and those of small-scale farms 11 percent. This means that family-scale farms are a slightly smaller percentage of all commercial farms (about 78 percent in 1950 instead of 82 percent in 1930).

Implications of trends in numbers. As between the commercial and the noncommercial part-time and residential groups, it may be

TABLE 4-3.—TRENDS IN NUMBERS OF FARMS BY MAJOR GROUPS, 1930 TO 1950

Year	All farms	Commercial farms [1]	Part-time and residential farms
	Thousands	*Thousands*	*Thousands*
1930......	6,289	5,282	1,007
1940......	6,097	4,717	1,380
1945......	5,859	4,186	1,673
1950......	5,379	3,706	1,673

Index 1930 = 100

Year	All farms	Commercial farms	Part-time and residential farms
1930......	100	100	100
1940......	97	89	137
1945......	93	79	166
1950......	86	70	166

NOTE.—For detailed methods used in preparing estimates, see Kenneth L. Bachman, "Changes in Commercial Farming and Their Implications," *Journal of Farm Economics*, May 1952; Jackson V. McElveen and Kenneth L. Bachman, "Low Production Farms," *U. S. Dept. Agr. Inf. Bul. 108*, June 1953.

[1] Includes farms classified as unusual-noncommercial in 1950.

TABLE 4-4.—TRENDS IN COMMERCIAL FARMS, BY SCALE GROUPS, 1930 TO 1950

Year	All commercial farms [1]	Large-scale farms	Family-scale farms	Small-scale farms
	Thousands	*Thousands*	*Thousands*	*Thousands*
1930......	5,282	128	4,356	798
1940......	4,717	119	3,718	880
1945......	4,186	117	3,284	785
1950......	3,706	103	2,886	717

Index 1930 = 100

Year	All commercial farms	Large-scale farms	Family-scale farms	Small-scale farms
1930......	100	100	100	100
1940......	89	93	85	110
1945......	79	91	75	98
1950......	70	80	66	89

See NOTE, table 4-3.

[1] Includes farms classified as unusual-noncommercial in 1950.

that the apparent upward trend in numbers of the latter is exaggerated somewhat by two factors. First, the varying definitions of a census farm, coupled with variations in the price level, may have meant failure to count as farms in earlier years some places that were included in later censuses. Second, application of the same index of output per man-hour to all economic classes and groups in adjusting class limits for earlier years may have caused too many residential farms to be counted as small-scale commercial farms. These uncertainties cannot be entirely resolved.

But if the estimates are taken as they stand it is clear that there are divergent trends. For this and other reasons it is desirable to handle commercial and noncommercial farms in separate groups. Even though the estimates given may be in error to some extent, it is probable that the directions indicated are approximately correct.

Within commercial farms, the differential rates of decrease between large-scale, family-scale, and small-scale farms are startling, but they are not to be considered as proof of economic superiority or inferiority. Bachman's examination of the question of relative efficiency led him to say that the "superiority of large-scale farms cannot be taken for granted." He came to the conclusion that the greater downward trend in the number of family-scale farms was due to greater upward flexibility in adding both capital and land to the relatively fixed family labor resources. Large-scale farms may already have used more of their potential flexibility.

The greater relative reduction in the number of family-scale farms, therefore, does not necessarily mean reduction in the proportion of total resources at the command of these farmers. Analysis on this point is incomplete, but the evidence available suggests that in 1950 family-scale farms controlled nearly the same proportion of all land and other resources used in farming as they did in 1930. Large-scale farms may even have lost a little ground in recent years. Large-scale farms have different trends in different parts of the country and in some regions. For example, those in the Corn Belt have not adjusted to some conditions as readily as have family-scale farms. Most modern farm machines are made in sizes that are about as efficient on family-scale as on large-scale farms. Only a few major exceptions are found. For instance, in irrigated cotton farming the large cotton pickers may favor large-scale operations.[6]

Small-scale farms present a special challenge; apparently they respond to pressures for change more slowly than do other commercial farms. The rate of change of about 11 percent indicated from 1940 to

---

[6] The apparent trend of farms in some size categories in the South may be related to the sharp reduction in numbers of sharecroppers. Several former sharecropper units, once counted as family-scale units, when joined to the home unit and operated with wage labor, might then be counted as a large-scale farm.

1950 is fairly substantial, and, if continued, it would ultimately bring the problem under control. Perhaps in certain locations some of these farms will become part-time farms with enough supplementary income to raise the whole income level enough to support a reasonable plane of living. The problems of rural poverty are real, but they can be solved. The way in which the situation has worked itself out in the northern Lake States region is instructive. Various combinations of public and private effort during the years have combined to do the job there. Much time and effort was used in the process of trial and error, and to minimize this expense and to speed the transition in other areas should be one objective of farm policy.

A review of the scanty resources at the command of people on small-scale farms, and even on small family-scale farms, shows that this is more than an agricultural problem alone.

The special problems of small-scale and small family-scale farms should not blind us to the adjustment problems of commercial farms in general and especially to those of family-scale farms that produce the bulk of the farm output.

Under some exceptional conditions large-scale farming appears to have certain economic advantages. To the extent that this advantage results from employment of wage hands whose alternatives are limited by poverty and lack of education, the gradual elimination of these underlying conditions and the improved alternatives for such people might be expected to remove a basic reason for this kind of large-scale farming. To the extent that such farming is based on other advantages, it may be permanently more economical in certain types of farming in restricted areas in which adequate supervision can be advantageous and in which certain economies of marketing and buying may be more available to large operators. But these advantages are likely to be more limited in future, as more farm tasks are either brought under technological control on family-scale farms, are taken away from the farm and performed in manufacturing plants under controlled conditions, or are available on a custom basis about equally efficiently for all sizes of operation.

Multiple units. A brief explanation of multiple units is necessary at this point. This involves an ancient form of tenure. It arose spontaneously in many parts of the world as an aftermath of feudalism. In this country it grew out of conditions following 1865 when landholders and former slaves both suffered from shortages of capital.

Multiple-unit operation is a pattern of farm operation that is not common in this country except in certain parts of the South. The arrangement is one in which the operator usually provides land, power, equipment, and general management for the operation, and the tenant receives a share of the crop for his work. Frequently subsistence credit is also "furnished" the tenant. Many variations and gradations in the arrangement are found, but in general the entire operation is handled as one business unit from the viewpoint of organization and management. Looked at in this way, the "croppers," as tenants in this system are termed, are really hired workers paid in shares of the crop. Under census procedure, however, sharecropping is customarily considered a form of tenancy and such operations are reported as separate farms. This means that what may really be only one management-farm or operational unit is reported as two or more census farms—the "home farm" is counted as one farm, and each cropper unit constitutes another.

For some purposes, it matters little whether multiple units are handled together or separately. For others, comparisons with farms of similar size in other areas are likely to lead to logical difficulties on either basis. But the concept of the "operational unit" or "economic firm" is significant when one thinks of the problems of farm organization and the opportunities for adjustment. The operator makes these decisions on the basis of the whole business for which he is responsible. The cropper has comparatively little to say about major adjustments, other than making the same kinds of decisions that confront a wage hand. He can choose between alternative opportunities for employment on and off the farm, but he cannot greatly affect the decisions concerning farm organization.

Data on multiple-unit operations were collected for several censuses on various bases. For the 1950 Census, information was collected and tabulated for a multiple-unit area that includes most of the multiple-unit operations in the South. A special report on multiple-unit operations presents this information in detail.[7]

Multiple units are closely associated with production of the major cash crops of the South—cotton, tobacco, and peanuts. A somewhat similar arrangement has grown up in certain commercial-broiler areas in both the South and the North, but this is not clearly revealed by census statistics. Broiler arrangements are mainly between growers and large feed-dealers or "financiers" who have off-farm bases. In other words, there is no "home" farm to be picked up by the census enumerator. Also, in this instance, sharecroppers have a fairly secure and permanent farm base of operations—their land is not owned by financier-operators but by themselves or by third parties.

Number of operational units. In the area enumerated for multiple units in the South, the total number of census farms was 2.0 million, and, after putting together the multiple-unit operations, the number of operational units (multiple plus single units) was found to be 1.7

---

[7] Bureau of the Census, *Multiple-Unit Operations, U. S. Census of Agriculture: 1950*, Vol. 5, *Special Reports*, Part 2, 1952.

million, or about 15 percent less. This reduction varied considerably from area to area; for Mississippi it was nearly 30 percent.

The effect on national totals of adjusting census farms to operational units is not great, but it has importance for the southern states and especially for those states and areas in which cotton and tobacco are prominent. Data by economic classes for multiple units were not developed for the 1950 Census, but similar data from the 1945 Census show that the differential effect by economic classes is also significant. On an operational-unit basis the proportionate numbers of large-scale and large family-scale farms are increased appreciably. This improves somewhat the apparent organization and operating efficiency of farms in multiple-unit areas. But it does not change the income status of croppers and their families, nor does it change the fact that in cotton and tobacco farming improved technology has reduced labor inputs less than in other types of farming.

Characteristic multiple-unit operations are field-crop farms. Nearly three-fourths of all multiple units in the multiple-unit area in 1950 were cotton and tobacco farms, and more than 90 percent were field-crop farms of some type (see tabulation).

Type of farm	Percentage of all multiple- unit farms
	Percent
Total......................	100.0
Cotton........................	48.1
Tobacco.......................	25.3
Rice..........................	0.2
Peanut........................	1.2
Cotton-and-tobacco.............	7.1
Cotton-and-rice................	0.2
Cotton-and-peanut..............	5.4
Tobacco-and-peanut.............	0.9
Cotton-tobacco-and-peanut.......	2.4
Miscellaneous..................	9.2

There are only a few subunits in most multiple-unit operations. The average number of croppers per multiple unit for the whole area enumerated was about 2.25. With the home farm this would mean 3.25 subunits per multiple unit.

Economic classes of commercial farms

About two-thirds of the farms counted in the 1950 Census were commercial farms. Virtually all farm production for sale (97.5 percent) came from commercial farms. These 3.7 million farms had most of the farm resources. They had 88 percent of the land in farms and 88 percent of the value of land and buildings, and they incurred 96.5 percent of the expenditures for hired labor (table 4-5). Noncommercial

TABLE 4-5.—NUMBER OF FARMS, PERCENTAGE OF SPECIFIED RESOURCES AND VALUE OF FARM SALES, COMMERCIAL AND NONCOMMERCIAL FARMS, UNITED STATES, 1950

Economic class	Number of farms	Land in farms	Value of land and buildings	Expenditure for hired labor [1]	Value of farm products sold [1]
	Thousands	Percent	Percent	Percent	Percent
All farms..............	5,379	100.0	100.0	100.0	100.0
Commercial farms.....	3,706	88.1	87.6	96.5	97.5
Noncommercial farms..	1,673	11.9	12.4	3.5	2.5

[1] Data relate to the 1949 crop year.

farms were significant for other reasons, but, so far as farm production for sale was concerned, they were unimportant.

The separation between commercial and noncommercial farms is more fundamental than the further subdivision of commercial farms into economic classes. Commercial farms are primarily agricultural, whereas the orientation of the noncommercial farms is mainly outside agriculture. The agricultural aspect of these farms is incidental, and the operator's primary interest is in the farm as a home rather than as a place to make a living.[8] Division of commercial farms into six economic classes is to some extent an artificial classification made for convenience in analysis. Agriculture as a means of earning money is the primary interest of all operators of commercial farms. Differences between the six classes are mainly differences in degree rather than in kind.

Much of this chapter is concerned with the scale characteristics of commercial farms. As indicated earlier, the six economic or scale classes are set up in accordance with the level of value of farm sales. At the upper end are the few large-scale farms; at the lower end, the more numerous small-scale farms. In between lie the four classes of family-scale farms.

The relative place of each economic class in the commercial farm total is shown in table 4-6. Large-scale farms accounted for about a fourth of the land in farms and for a fourth of the value of products sold. Small-scale farms, although they made up nearly a fifth of all commercial farms, had only 6 percent of the land in farms and 2.4 percent of the value of products sold by commercial farms. Family-scale farms had the great bulk of both resources and sales.

[8] It is necessary to recognize that agriculture may not be the primary interest of some of those who operate commercial farms. Many livestock show farms, for example, are playthings even though highly profitable. The basis of the census classification is simply the size of the farming operations as measured by sales of farm products.

TABLE 4-6.—NUMBER OF FARMS, PERCENTAGE OF FARMS, SPECIFIED RESOURCES AND VALUE OF FARM SALES, BY ECONOMIC CLASS OF COMMERCIAL FARMS, UNITED STATES, 1950

Economic class	Number of farms		Land in farms	Value of land and buildings	Expenditure for hired labor [1]	Value of farm products sold [1]
	Thousands	*Percent*	*Percent*	*Percent*	*Percent*	*Percent*
All commercial.........	3,706	100.0	100.0	100.0	100.0	100.0
Large-scale farms....	103	2.8	24.5	17.3	41.5	26.7
Family-scale farms...	2,886	77.9	69.5	77.6	57.1	70.9
Large.............	381	10.3	21.1	24.0	25.6	25.4
Upper medium.....	721	19.5	21.1	25.2	17.3	23.3
Lower medium.....	882	23.8	16.5	17.7	9.6	14.7
Small.............	902	24.3	10.8	10.7	4.6	7.5
Small-scale farms.....	717	19.3	6.0	5.1	1.4	2.4

[1] Data relate to 1949 crop year.

Data on a per-farm basis show the average characteristics of the several classes (table 4-7). Each indicated resource reflects the range in size from small-scale to large-scale.

Large-scale farms stand out, especially in respect to their large expenditures for hired labor. The scale of operations and the heavy labor load indicate that operators of large farms spend much more of their time in management and supervisory activities.

By any measure family-scale farms form the great inner core of commercial farms. Size of business covers a wide range, but for the most part it is not so large as to exceed the capacity of family labor resources. On some family-scale farms the hired-labor bill is large, but in most cases this is supplementary to operator and family labor. Large family-scale farms averaged nearly 570 acres in 1950, upper and lower medium-scale farms had about 300 and 200 acres, and small family-scale farms about 125 acres of farmland. Around half of the land on family-scale farms was cropland. Value of land and buildings averaged from about $8,000 on small family-scale farms to more than $40,000 on large family-scale farms. The primary characteristic of family-scale farms is that responsibility for management, capital, and most of the labor is vested in the family itself. The farm family and the farm are closely identified.

Small-scale farms are places on which farming is the chief business, but on which there is not enough of it to provide a very good living. Land and capital are both insufficient to provide families with full-time remunerative employment on these farms. In some cases such farms

TABLE 4-7.—SPECIFIED RESOURCES, EXPENDITURE FOR HIRED LABOR, AND VALUE OF FARM SALES, AVERAGE PER FARM BY ECONOMIC CLASS, UNITED STATES, 1950

Economic class	Average per farm				
	Farm acreage		Value of land and buildings	Expenditure for hired labor [1]	Value of farm prod- ucts sold [1]
	All land	Crop- land			
	Acres	Acres	Dollars	Dollars	Dollars
All farms....................	215.6	89.1	13,911	450	4,142
Commercial farms..........	275.6	119.0	17,696	630	5,858
Large-scale..............	2,421.7	565.5	110,008	9,398	56,058
Family-scale.............	246.2	123.4	17,637	462	5,340
Large.................	566.8	259.6	41,318	1,568	14,475
Upper medium..........	298.2	162.0	22,918	560	7,017
Lower medium.........	191.2	99.9	13,162	254	3,625
Small.................	122.8	58.2	7,829	120	1,813
Small-scale..............	84.9	37.1	4,648	46	720
Noncommercial farms........	82.8	22.8	5,481	49	339
Part-time..............	75.6	30.2	6,117	53	612
Residential.............	50.0	17.0	4,675	21	82
Unusual................	9,178.9	316.9	105,795	6,195	21,446

[1] Data relate to the 1949 crop year.

may be operated by single individuals who have unusually low family obligations and whose more limited needs may thus be satisfied.

Division of commercial farms into the six scale classes is necessarily somewhat arbitrary, because the distribution of all commercial farms is quite continuous. Separation of small family-scale farms from small-scale farms at the bottom is based on an estimate of where to draw a line of demarcation ($1,200 of sales of farm products) below which incomes are surely too small to provide minimum support for a family.[9] Separation of large-scale farms at the upper end reflects judgment as to the scale of operation that would usually involve more labor than would be available on a family farm and that would require much of the operator's time for management.

The four classes of family-scale farms represent groupings that have rolled together a sufficient segment for convenient analysis. Beyond these considerations a certain mathematical logic is involved in the original design for the class boundaries, which makes each successive class interval cover roughly double the range of income included in the preceding one. This geometric relationship is visible again in the

[9] This was not intended to imply that $1,200 is enough.

average sales value of farm products sold from each economic class
(table 4-7). The principal exception is the large-scale class, in which
average sales of farm products at $56,000 are about 4 times the average
sales of the preceding large family-scale class. This result follows from
the open upper end of the large-scale class. It is necessary to remember that the total range in size, as measured by value of sales, is
several times as great for large-scale farms as for all other classes of
commercial farms combined. It runs from $25,000 to above $500,000.
The greater range means greater diversity in characteristics of large-
scale farms.

Geographic distribution of economic classes of farms. The geographic distribution of economic classes of farms shows a curious set of

FIGURE 4-2. COMMERCIAL FARMS, NUMBER, APRIL 1, 1950

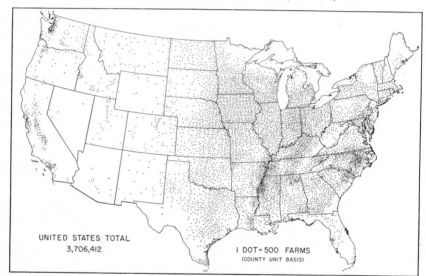

UNITED STATES TOTAL
3,706,412

I DOT = 500 FARMS
(COUNTY UNIT BASIS)

Source: Bureau of the Census.

patterns. One needs first to look at fig. 4-2, which shows the distribution of all commercial farms, in order to have a base pattern against
which to place each individual class. The relative density of farms in
the eastern half of the country and certain obvious concentrations are
evident at a glance.

With this background perspective, the six dot maps in figs. 4-3 and
4-4 can be viewed for the separate economic classes. Comparing the
six maps leads to tentative generalizations. Economic classes I, II, and
III are distributed in much the same general pattern, with heavier concentrations in the North, the Great Plains and the Pacific Coast. Economic class IV farms are more widely distributed. Economic classes

FIGURE 4-3. NUMBER OF FARMS IN ECONOMIC CLASSES I, II, AND III, APRIL 1, 1950

Economic Class I Farms (gross sales of $25,000 or more)

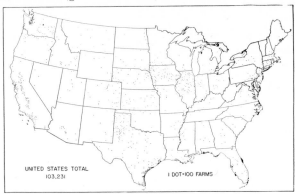

Economic Class II Farms (gross sales of $10,000 to $24,999)

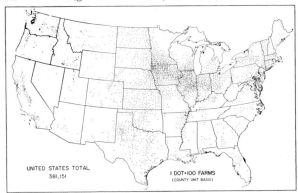

Economic Class III Farms (gross sales of $5,000 to $9,999)

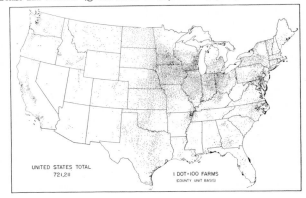

Source: Bureau of the Census.

FIGURE 4-4. NUMBER OF FARMS IN ECONOMIC CLASSES IV, V, AND VI, APRIL 1, 1950

Economic Class IV Farms (gross sales of $2,500 to $4,999)

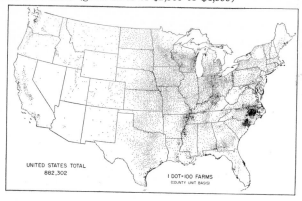

Economic Class V Farms (gross sales of $1,200 to $2,499)

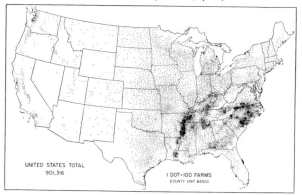

Economic Class VI Farms (gross sales of $250 to $1,199, farm products major source of income. Operator working off farm less than 100 days and income from sale of farm products greater than family income from other source)

Source: Bureau of the Census.

V and VI—small family-scale and small-scale farms—have areas of special density in the Appalachian and Southern States. These summary generalizations apply only to major concentrations; some farms of each class are found in every region.

Why should these marked differences in geographic distribution of economic classes show up? We recognize the need for a patterned range in farm sizes to fit the range in management ability of operators, the stages in the life cycles of farm families, variations in family numbers, differences in willingness to work hard, and other considerations. But one might expect this to be achieved without such pronounced area and regional differences. Geographic differences are direct evidence of relative differences in mobility of people and resources.

Much of the explanation lies in the history of each area and in institutional factors. Differences in basic resources, in available capital, in characteristics of commodities, and in types of farming account for friction and slowness in making necessary adjustments. Unless there are off-farm opportunities for excess population, adjustments toward more economical sizes of farms takes place with glacial slowness. The presence of such off-farm opportunities in some areas and not in others during the last few decades, especially since 1940, accounts for many of the differences in rates of adjustment.

Because of their small numbers, large-scale (class I) farms present a pattern on the dot map that is less clear than those of other classes. Large-scale farms are most numerous in the Pacific States, the western Corn Belt, and the Southern Plains, but there are a few nearly everywhere.

Large family-scale and upper-medium family-scale farms (classes II and III) are found especially in the Corn Belt, the Lake States, and the Northwest. Class III concentrations are particularly great in Wisconsin, Minnesota, and the eastern Corn Belt. These two classes of farms accounted for nearly half of all sales of farm products.

Lower-medium family-scale farms (class IV) are widely distributed, but they have higher densities in North Carolina and South Carolina. Despite this southern orientation, more of the farms in this class are in the North rather than in the South.

Small family-scale farms and small-scale farms (classes V and VI) are heavily concentrated in the Appalachian and Southern States. They are closely associated with production of cotton and tobacco. Large numbers are also found in other parts of the country.

Large-scale farms

In this age of large-scale business, many people think of large-scale farms as Paul Bunyan operations. The more colorful examples of very large farming ventures that make headlines tend to reinforce this impression. But the truth is that giant farms are exceptions. Average large-scale farms, as classified by the census, are rather small as compared with much of urban business, even though they are large among farms. A factory with less than a dozen workers on the payroll, an annual wage bill of $9,000, and total yearly sales of $56,000 would be thought small business indeed. Yet this is about what large-scale farms averaged in 1949.

The census definition for large-scale (class I) farms took in all farms with $25,000 or more of sales of farm products in 1949. This included a little more than 100,000 farms, or the top 3 percent of all commercial farms (2 percent of all farms). Although the percentage of hired managers was higher for large-scale farms, more than 9 in 10 of these farms were operated by owners or tenants. From the normal viewpoint of urban business, large-scale farms are mainly small "family businesses," that is to say, they are under the control and direction of a single family and are not like corporations in structure. In effect, most large-scale farms are upward extensions of family-scale farms and in many respects they behave like them.

It should be kept in mind that, although we speak of average large-scale farms, the dispersion among them in size and probably in other characteristics is greater than for all other classes of commercial farms combined. As a class, large-scale farms are far more heterogeneous than other economic classes of farms. As mentioned earlier, it is something like the dispersion that one would find in studying mountains between various levels of elevation. If we substitute hundreds of feet for thousands of dollars, we can see that the dispersion above the 2,500-foot level of elevation will be much greater than that below, when individual peaks rise to more than 50,000 feet.

The over-all significance of the 103,000 large-scale farms in the agricultural economy is shown by the large share of the value of farm products sold, 26 percent (table 4-8). In the respective product groups, large-scale farms supplied about half of the total sales of fruits and nuts, and vegetables, and more than a third of all cattle and calves. They accounted for 40 percent of the expenditures for hired labor and livestock and poultry.

The composition of all large-scale farms by type shows that there are relatively more livestock, poultry, vegetable, and fruit-and-nut farms than is true for all commercial farms (table 4-9). There are fewer crop and dairy farms. More than a third of all large-scale farms are livestock farms. If all livestock types—dairy, poultry, and general—are added together, something more than half of all large-scale farms are included.

TABLE 4-8.—PERCENTAGE OF THE TOTAL VALUE OF FARM PRODUCTS SOLD AND OF SELECTED EXPENDITURES ACCOUNTED FOR BY LARGE-SCALE FARMS, 1949

Item	Percentage of total sales or expenditures
	Percent
Sales:	
All farm products...............	26.0
Field crops....................	22.5
Vegetables.....................	55.1
Fruits and nuts................	45.9
Dairy products.................	13.7
Poultry and poultry products.....	22.9
Cattle and calves..............	37.2
Hogs and pigs..................	11.4
Expenditures:	
Hired labor....................	40.1
Feed purchased................	23.2
Livestock and poultry purchased..	39.9

TABLE 4-9.—DISTRIBUTION OF LARGE-SCALE FARMS AND ALL COMMERCIAL FARMS BY TYPE, UNITED STATES, 1950

Type of farm	Large-scale farms	All commercial farms
	Percent	*Percent*
Field-crop.....	28.9	39.1
Vegetable......	3.0	1.3
Fruit-and-nut..	5.1	2.2
Dairy.........	9.7	16.2
Poultry.......	8.4	4.7
Livestock [1]....	35.7	21.8
General.......	5.0	13.3
Miscellaneous..	4.2	1.4
Total.......	100.0	100.0

[1] Livestock other than dairy and poultry.

Geographic distribution. The large-scale farm dot map in fig. 4-3 shows the distribution of large-scale farms in this country. Concentrations appear in Illinois, Iowa, the Texas High Plains, and irrigated areas in California. But this view needs to be supplemented with fig. 4-5, which indicates the relative position of large-scale farms among all commercial farms in each state. Large-scale farms in Illinois and

FIGURE 4-5. LARGE-SCALE (CLASS I) FARMS AS A PERCENTAGE OF COMMERCIAL FARMS, BY STATES, 1950

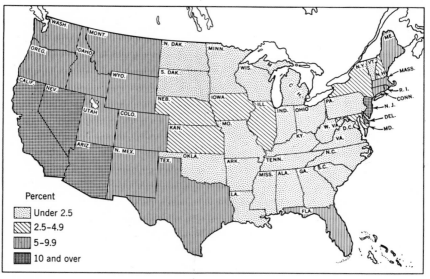

Source: Data are from Bureau of the Census.

Iowa stand out on the dot map, but they represent only about 4 percent of all commercial farms in these states. They appear numerous because all farms are numerous there.

Large-scale farms are relatively more numerous in the Western States, the Northeast, and Florida. Lowest percentages are in the South. In terms of value of products sold, large-scale farms produced more than 60 percent of the value of farm products sold in California, Nevada, Arizona, and Florida in 1949. The percentage of sales from large-scale farms was also high in the Mountain States. Percentages in the Southeast and the Central States were lower.

Kinds of large-scale farms. Various methods have been suggested for grouping large-scale farms in accordance with resource utilization, especially with reference to labor. Bachman and Jones, for example, present three broad groups.[10]

---

[10] Kenneth L. Bachman and Ronald W. Jones, "Sizes of Farms in the United States," *U. S. Dept. Agr. Tech. Bul. 1019,* July 1950, p. 35.

1. Large-scale highly mechanized units.
2. Large-scale wage-operated units.
3. Large-scale tenant plantations or multiple units.

We must understand "highly mechanized" in this sense as referring to all the technology and knowledge invested in farming. It is more than the power and machinery so important in crop farming; it includes other kinds of capital goods and improved practices used with both crops and livestock. Obviously there is a close relationship between types of farming, the state of technology in different lines of production, and the scale of organization.

Highly mechanized large-scale farms include both field-crop and livestock farms of the Corn Belt and Plains States where natural conditions are favorable to high mechanization and to a high level of technology with respect to livestock. Large-scale cattle-and-hog-feeding operations in the Corn Belt and elsewhere are among those included. In commercial-broiler areas many individual units are large enough to be classed as large-scale farms. The state of Delaware illustrates this situation.

Many of these large-scale, highly mechanized farms are only a little above family-scale farms from the viewpoint of labor employed. In Iowa, for example, large-scale farms reported an average of about one regular hired worker per farm and about $2,200 annually spent for labor. In California, on the other hand, the average expenditure for hired labor per large-scale farm was about $19,000.

In essence, large-scale highly mechanized farms are super-family-scale farms whose operators have unusual ability, capital means, or fortuity. In a prosperous economy with reasonable flexibility of resources a certain proportion of this kind of large-scale farming would be expected as a normal part of the agricultural scene. In a balanced economy the structure should be kept open for persons of exceptional ability to find such farming opportunities to the same extent as in industry. Otherwise, they may be attracted to other lines of activity that offer greater personal rewards but permit less contribution to the national welfare.

Large-scale wage-operated units are represented by some of the fruit-and-nut farms and some of the vegetable farms in California, Texas, Florida, and elsewhere. They also include farms in the Mountain States that grow intensive labor crops like sugar beets and potatoes under irrigation. A high level of mechanization at some stages of production may be combined with very high labor inputs at others. Cotton production in irrigated areas and in the Delta States is in a partially mechanized transition stage.

In irrigated areas, very high yields simplify the problem of supervision of labor, because the farms are smaller and the work is less spread out in space. Perhaps the most difficult management problem is related to the seasonal distribution of peak workloads. Further development of mechanization and improved technology may relieve such bottlenecks.

The third group of large-scale farms—the large-scale plantation or multiple unit—is fading into history as mechanization and other opportunities for labor increase. Because the census counts cropper units as farms, this kind of large-scale farm is not well reflected in the scale classification. The special report on multiple units for 1950 does not classify multiple units by economic class. Comparisons with the 1945 Census, in which this was done, indicate that an appreciable number of large-scale farms would have been added in 1950. But the total is not large, as most multiple units are not large enough to be classed as large-scale farms.

Family-scale farms

Family-scale farms make up the main body of commercial farms after the relatively few large-scale farms and the more numerous but very small, small-scale farms are separated out. In 1950 family-scale farms comprised nearly 80 percent of all commercial farms and had about 70 percent of the value of products sold. A large part of agricultural policy and program making is therefore directly concerned with these middle groups of farms.

Family-scale farms extend over a much narrower range in size than do large-scale farms, although the spread from $1,200 to $25,000 in value of products sold is broad enough to justify further separation into the four subclasses.

Geographic distribution. The geographic distribution of family-scale farms in each of the several classes is noted on the dot maps in figs. 4-3 and 4-4. Relative numbers of family-scale farms by states have a definite regional pattern also (fig. 4-6). The northern half of the country has the highest percentage of family-scale farms. In Wisconsin, Minnesota, Iowa, North Dakota, South Dakota, Nebraska, and Vermont, more than 90 percent of all commercial farms are in the family-scale group. In a number of the southern states only half to two-thirds of the commercial farms are family-scale. In the southern Plains, the Southwest, and California, the proportion of family-scale farms is held at around 75 percent by the presence of many large-scale farms.

In addition to these general differences, more family-scale farms in the North and West are in the upper size classes than those in the tobacco and cotton areas of the South.

Characteristics of family-scale farms. General characteristics of family-scale farms as opposed to large-scale and small-scale farms have been noted. The uneven evolution of farming in different areas and regions with different resources and opportunities has given rise to many differences in family-scale farms. Some would say that they are mainly related to types of farming. The technical circumstances surrounding production of different crops or livestock certainly influence the physical size of the operation that a farm operator and family can handle. But if competitive forces were fully effective and if resources

FIGURE 4-6. FAMILY-SCALE (CLASSES II, III, IV, AND V) FARMS AS A PERCENTAGE OF COMMERCIAL FARMS, BY STATES, 1950

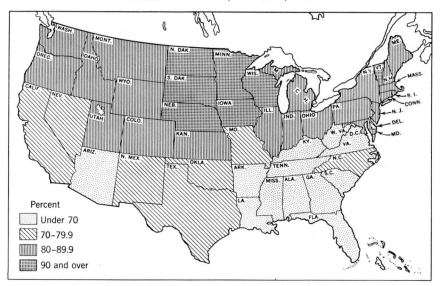

Source: Data are from Bureau of the Census.

moved freely into their most productive uses, the differences between regions and areas would be much less than those that actually prevail.

At the risk of anticipating later discussions of types of farming, we can perhaps best describe some of the characteristics of family-scale farms by referring to estimates drawn from a special study of commercial family-operated farms in nineteen selected type-of-farming areas.[11] Each of these farms is an average family-scale farm of the indicated type in its respective area. Selected characteristics of these nineteen types of farms as of 1947–1949 illustrate the wide differences found in the several regions (table 4-10).

At one extreme we find the hog-beef-fattening farms in the Corn Belt and the irrigated cotton farms in the Texas High Plains. They have high investments and high gross incomes. Wheat-pea farms in

---

11 Agricultural Research Service, "Farm Costs and Returns, 1953 (With Comparisons)." *U. S. Dept. Agr. Inf. Bul. 128*, 1954.

TABLE 4–10.—FARM SIZE CHARACTERISTICS OF NINETEEN AVERAGE COMMERCIAL FAMILY-OPERATED FARMS, SELECTED AREAS, AVERAGE 1947–1949

Type of farm and location	Total land in farm	Total labor used	Total invest- ment	Return to operator and family [1]
	Acres	*Hours*	*Dollars*	*Dollars*
Dairy farms:				
Central Northeast...............................	189	5,240	21,470	2,801
Eastern Wisconsin...............................	120	5,330	27,350	3,037
Western Wisconsin..............................	136	4,750	18,270	2,394
Corn Belt farms:				
Hog-dairy......................................	158	4,550	32,440	4,130
Hog-beef-raising...............................	204	3,380	26,050	2,162
Hog-beef-fattening.............................	192	4,420	46,930	8,470
Cash-grain.....................................	222	3,460	63,100	6,051
Tobacco-livestock farms:				
Kentucky bluegrass.............................	113	4,190	19,050	2,414
Cotton farms:				
Southern Piedmont..............................	161	4,450	11,290	965
Delta of Mississippi............................	45	3,730	8,830	2,392
Black Prairie, Texas............................	157	5,080	17,220	2,257
High Plains, Texas (nonirrigated)................	309	4,580	28,870	5,003
High Plains, Texas (irrigated)...................	271	6,930	47,290	8,456
Spring-wheat farms (Northern Plains):				
Wheat-small-grain-livestock.....................	621	3,280	31,090	4,822
Wheat-corn-livestock...........................	460	3,900	31,520	4,327
Winter-wheat farms:				
Wheat-pea (Washington and Idaho)...............	481	3,150	103,270	6,854
Sheep ranches:				
Northern Plains................................	5,119	7,450	66,740	3,481
Cattle ranches:				
Northern Plains................................	3,800	4,330	59,640	3,396
Intermountain region...........................	1,615	4,790	67,490	5,550

[1] For labor and management.

Source: Agricultural Research Service, "Farm Costs and Returns, 1953 (With Comparisons)," *U. S. Dept. Agr. Inf. Bul. 128, 1954.*

the Pacific Northwest and cash-grain farms in the Corn Belt are good-size businesses also. They are mechanized and expenditures for labor are relatively low.

At the other extreme are the small cotton farms in the South. These farms represent a much lower investment, a high labor input, and a distinctly transitional technology. Some operations are mechanized, but hand work in hoeing and picking is still the rule.

Some of the differences shown in table 4-10 reflect income conditions of the given years and will not persist, but the differences in returns are too great to suggest that distribution of opportunities has been equal.

Small-scale farms

Small-scale farms are units with value of sales between $250 and $1,200, with operators working off the farm less than 100 days, and with family income from nonfarm sources less than that from farm sales. If either of the last two limitations was exceeded, the farm was classed as a part-time farm.   Gross income within these limits in most cases would be inadequate to support a reasonable level of living as understood by most of our citizens.   No doubt some farms in this class had more income in earlier years and will rise in the economic scale again. In some cases there may have been unreported income.   But in any event these are extremely small commercial farms, and they represent a major problem in the agricultural economy.   More than 717,000, or 19 percent, of all commercial farms were classified as small-scale.

Geographic distribution.   The earlier small-scale-farm dot map (fig. 4-4) shows the concentration of small-scale farms in the Appalachian

FIGURE 4-7. SMALL-SCALE (CLASS VI) FARMS AS A PERCENTAGE OF COMMERCIAL FARMS, BY STATES, 1950

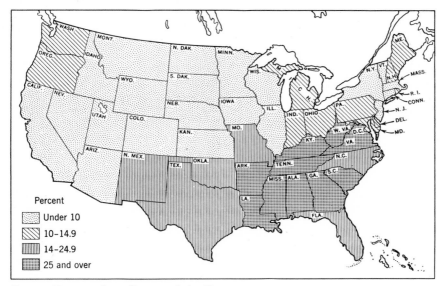

Percent
Under 10
10–14.9
14–24.9
25 and over

Source: Data are from Bureau of the Census.

and Southern States.   The same fact is brought out on a relative basis in fig. 4-7.   The association with cotton and tobacco types of farming is clear.   Large numbers are found in the hilly Appalachian area, too.

Efficiency and scale of operation

Farms in this country have grown larger as measured by number of acres.   For example, numbers of farms with 1,000 or more acres for successive decennial census years since 1900 are given in the accompanying tabulation.

Year	Thousand farms
1900.........	47
1910.........	50
1920.........	67
1930.........	81
1940.........	100
1950.........	121

Statistics like these have alarmed many people who have not fully appreciated the normal growth in size of business that technology has permitted for farms in all size classes.[12] As we have seen, there are actually fewer large-scale farms than formerly. What has happened is that all farms have grown larger, because labor is more effectively employed, with more capital equipment.

Much has been written concerning the relative efficiency of different scales of operation. Some range in size is probably necessary to permit the best use of the variation in natural capabilities found among farm operators. Some operators are more efficient on small farms, others on large. Thus, even if there were *no* differences in the relative technical efficiency of farms of different sizes, a pattern of different sizes would make more efficient use of managerial resources. Beyond this, the argument must run in terms of technical efficiency. If large-scale farms should be found to use resources more effectively than family-scale farms, we would probably accept them as we have their counterparts in urban business. Social advantages that grow out of wide distribution of the management function in farm production would be sought in other ways. With present-day transportation and communication this would doubtless be feasible. A modern equivalent of the "enclosure movement" might be permitted if it were more productive and if it were accompanied by countervailing forces to protect farm people.[13]

So far there appears to be no very convincing proof that large-scale farms are any more efficient than family-scale farms. Such research as has been directed to the problem apparently suggests the contrary for most types of farming, when all factors, including management, are taken into account. Elements involved differ in significance from place to place. They include the following:

1. Higher costs of supervision over larger areas as balanced against gains from specialization in tasks.

---

12 Many of these farms with more than 1,000 acres are in western dryland areas, where a family with modern machinery can easily handle such acreages.

13 "Enclosure" is a term used to describe division of common fields, pastures, and meadows into consolidated individual farm holdings with fences around the separate holdings. Enclosure movements in England, for example, took place mainly from 1485 to 1600 and from 1760 to 1815. They replaced feudal village farming of small strips owned in common with larger, more efficient farms.

2. State of technology in particular lines of production, especially efficiency of different sizes and kinds of machines, and divisibility of key resources.

3. Relative ability to withstand risks.

4. Relative advantages in buying, selling, financing, research, and other activities.

Use of farm sales as a basis for the scale classification, makes it difficult to learn much from census data about the relative efficiency of large-scale farms. Size and efficiency factors are so intertwined in the measure of scale that, although the larger sizes apparently show greater efficiency, this is a built-in statistical phenomenon rather than a real relationship. We must therefore turn to evidence from other sources.

Empirical research directly on the problem of scale in farming is limited. But two recent studies by Scoville and Fellows throw some light on the subject. Scoville's study relates to corn-livestock farming in Nebraska.[14] Fellows and his associates analyzed dairying in New England.[15] The types of farming in the two areas are quite different.

In substance both found comparatively little additional economy from scale, once a well-organized, fully employed one-man unit had been achieved. Scoville's analysis included five levels of scale as compared with Fellows' four levels. Scoville's top level also went higher and into the large-scale class. At this level he found some measurable economy of scale, but if the management factor was evaluated proportionally the economy largely disappeared. Individual machine costs showed rapidly decreasing costs up to a certain level and then very moderate further changes. Most farm machines are now made in sizes that will fit a fully employed one-man farm. For those that do not, the possibility of custom-hire offers a relatively low-cost alternative.

It is often alleged that many farm tasks need several men for most efficient performance. But Scoville's analysis of forty-five specific operational farm tasks found that most of them could be done as efficiently by one man or one man and a boy as by more. The few tasks that could not be handled in this way could be done by exchanging work with a neighbor.

From this research one must conclude that scale offers little economy or diseconomy for types similar to those studied. The main thing is to get as good an adjustment of resources as possible at any particular level.

These two studies were budget studies—economic engineering at-

---

14 Orlin J. Scoville, "Relationships Between Size of Farm and Utilization of Machinery, Equipment, and Labor on Nebraska Corn-Livestock Farms," *U. S. Dept. Agr. Tech. Bul. 1037*, Sept. 1951.

15 I. F. Fellows, G. E. Frick, and S. B. Weeks, "Production Efficiency on New England Dairy Farms," 2. "Economies of Scale in Dairying—An Exploration in Farm Management Research Methodology," *Storrs Agr. Expt. Sta. Bul. 285*, Feb. 1952.

tempts to test the scale effect, with extraneous factors held in abeyance. What about actual conditions? Many farm-management studies have shown that a larger size of business is accompanied by higher returns. In most instances, other factors have been intercorrelated so that the real meaning of the findings with respect to economy of scale has been in question. Often the larger farms were on better land, or had more efficient managers or better equipment, so that apparent returns to size may not have been the result of scale.

Heady, with some new statistical methods, has found either slightly decreasing or constant returns to increased scale with several sets of Iowa farm data.[16] He points out the heterogeneous nature of the resources in the samples used, the lack of measurement of management as an input, and other shortcomings. Such findings are thus incomplete evidence. But they are apparently in line with the budget studies.

The general conclusion from theoretical reasoning, budget studies, and statistical approaches is that economies of scale are doubtful. There may be some exceptions in certain types of farming. But even then the exceptions may represent situations that are temporary in nature or that may be redressed with more capital or more careful organization.

Risk and efficiency. In many respects farming is a high-risk industry. Fluctuations in yields and in prices are the two great risks. Something has been done about both of these in recent years, but important risks must be expected to remain, especially in certain areas and in specific types of farming. The relationship between risk and scale of farming has not been fully explored. In general, the immediate impact of adverse yield or price fluctuations is proportionately greater on large-scale than on smaller farms, because the greater cash outlay for hired labor and perhaps other items means that the margin between cash receipts and cash expenses is narrower. Bachman and Jones, for example, tested the effects of a 15-percent reduction in prices on a family-scale and a large-scale farm in the Northern Plains and found that the operator's net income would be reduced 16 and 26 percent respectively.[17] In some types of farming, large-scale operators might be in better position to meet risks because of larger capital reserves or better access to credit facilities.

Note on economies of scale. Textbooks contain discussion about "true economies of scale" as contrasted with "economies of proportionality." A "true" change in scale is said to be one in which all input factors are in homogeneous and divisible form and are kept in equal proportions, that is, the proportional relationships between factors are

---

16 Earl O. Heady, "Technical Scale Relationships and Farm Size Policy," *The Southern Economic Journal,* Jan. 1953, pp. 353–364.

17 Bachman and Jones, *op. cit.*

kept constant as input levels are raised or lowered. This is a rather fine-spun academic definition that is useful as an analytic device in classroom teaching but is of limited validity in practice. Factors seldom come in homogeneous and divisible form capable of being combined in constant proportions. To the extent that they do so, constant returns may be expected.

Favorite examples of economies or diseconomies of scale involve the physical laws of geometry which are represented by the properties of plane surfaces and solids. A 2-inch water pipe carries four times and not twice the volume of water carried by a 1-inch pipe. A superscale grasshopper would not be able to jump the Washington Monument because its weight would increase by the cube of a single dimensional increase and pin it to earth. But examples like these merely point up the physical impossibility of increasing inputs in constant proportions.

Division of labor and specialization are sometimes suggested as bona fide instances of economies of scale. But, if so, there is relatively little opportunity for them to develop on most farms.

Common sense therefore tells us not to worry about true economies of scale but to consider the economies or diseconomies that may arise with operations at different levels of input, recognizing that most of them arise from so-called proportionality adjustments.

CHAPTER 5

STRUCTURE OF COMMERCIAL FARMS—TYPE

Types of commercial farms

Size and type are the touchstones for describing farms. In these measures we use an almost universal scheme of classification, which tries to answer the twin questions of *How large?* and *What kind?* Think how often and how naturally this binary system presents itself in every-day affairs. Jones wears shoes that are 9D brown oxfords; Smith's car is equipped with 6.00 × 16 low-pressure tires; White lives in a 7-room rambler. Each of these statements is a brief description of size and type that gives essential information.

Economic classes of farms provide us with a useful dimensional view of commercial farms. The *How large?*, or scale, part of the problem is well answered. But the total view is likely to be obscured and colorless unless it is supplemented by the *What kind?* member. The type classification breathes life into the cold statistics and shows more clearly the nature of the farms that make up the commercial agriculture of the Nation.

In dealing with problems of farm policy and farm adjustment, size and type are both significant. Partly because the differences between types are frequently related to geography, the type has usually preceded the scale classification in analyzing adjustment problems. In one sense, type may represent more fundamental differences than scale. The accounting system in the city zoo might find it desirable to classify animals on the basis of size in order to analyze costs of feeding. Its budget might usefully reflect costs for large, medium, and small animals. But zoologists would first classify the animals by types (genera and families).

The close relationship between types of farming and the geography of agricultural resources was pointed out in Chapter 3. The succession of visible variations in types is evident to anyone who has traveled across any extensive part of the country. Although many types of farming may occur within an area, one or two usually predominate. A preliminary impression of the extent of this specialization may be obtained by classifying the counties in the United States by major sources

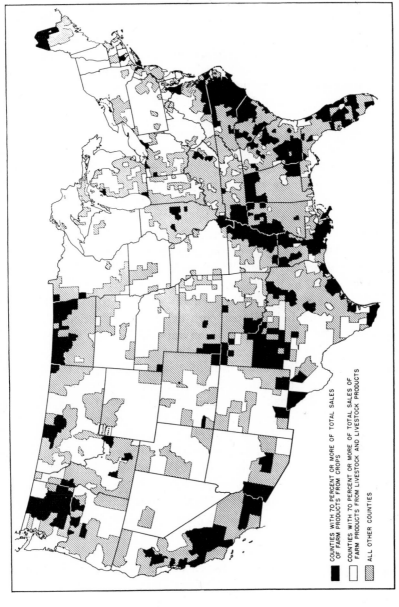

FIGURE 5-1. COUNTIES CLASSIFIED BY MAJOR SOURCE OF FARM INCOME, 1950

COUNTIES WITH 70 PERCENT OR MORE OF TOTAL SALES OF FARM PRODUCTS FROM CROPS

COUNTIES WITH 70 PERCENT OR MORE OF TOTAL SALES OF FARM PRODUCTS FROM LIVESTOCK AND LIVESTOCK PRODUCTS

ALL OTHER COUNTIES

Source: Bureau of the Census.

of farm income as between crops and livestock (fig. 5-1). Counties shown in black are those with 70 percent or more of their 1949 sales of farm products from crops. Those in white are those with 70 percent or more of their sales of farm products from livestock and livestock products. Counties that have diagonal lines are the ones that fall between these limits. On this basis, livestock areas are somewhat more extensive than crop areas. Also, they are more in the northern and western parts of the country. The influence of rainfall, temperature, and other natural conditions on production of grass and forage crops has much to do with the location of large segments of the livestock enterprise.

Cash-crop areas probably include an even greater variety of situations than livestock areas. An obvious reason is that there are many more kinds of crops than of livestock in commercial production. Each crop reacts in its own way to soils and climate. The predominance of crops is therefore more scattered, and some of this is reflected in the map. Looking across the map, one can pick out Aroostook County, Maine, the intensive potato area in the Northeast; the Palouse wheat and irrigated fruit areas in the Pacific Northwest; the spring wheat area in North Dakota; the Delta cotton area in the lower Mississippi valley; California's great irrigated Central Valley; Georgia's peanut and tobacco area; and many others.

Livestock areas also include such diverse situations as dairying in the Northeast and Lake States, corn-hog-beef production in the Midwest, and cattle ranching and sheep ranching in the Western States. Livestock farming includes many distinct types.

The kind of division shown in fig. 5-1 is an initial step toward a type classification. But one cannot be content with merely a tripartite arrangement. A reasonably satisfactory classification must have more subdivisions, though not so many that it will become too bulky for national aggregation. Many type classifications have been devised by census workers and other researchers over the years. The census alone used different schemes in 1930, 1940, 1945, and again in 1950.

The making of type classifications has been compared to what happens when a toy kaleidoscope is disturbed. Each time the kaleidoscope is shaken the same bits of colored glass form a beautiful new pattern. The classification pattern that emerged in the 1950 shakedown is shown in table 5-1 and fig. 5-2. One should not be too much disturbed by the analogy of the kaleidoscope. It reflects an elementary truth in that there is no one best way of classifying types, especially in terms of a few national aggregates. With changing circumstances we may again have alterations. The 1950 Census defines 12 types on the general basis of the product or group of products amounting to 50 percent or more of the value of all products sold from the farm.

FIGURE 5-2. TYPE-OF-FARMING AREAS. 1950

[Based on the type accounting for 50 percent or more of commercial farms within each county]

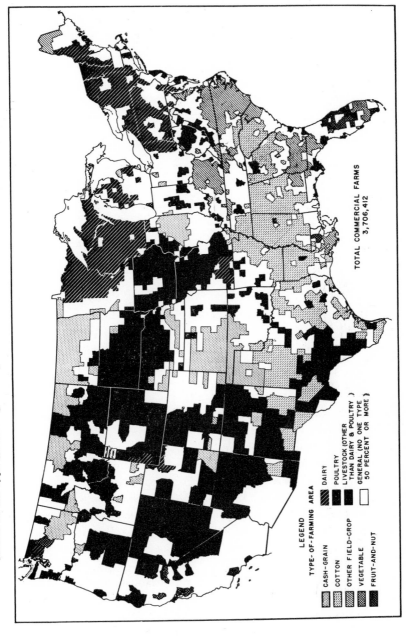

LEGEND
TYPE-OF-FARMING AREA

CASH-GRAIN
COTTON
OTHER FIELD-CROP
VEGETABLE
FRUIT-AND-NUT
DAIRY
POULTRY
LIVESTOCK (OTHER
THAN DAIRY & POULTRY)
GENERAL (NO ONE TYPE
50 PERCENT OR MORE)

TOTAL COMMERCIAL FARMS
3,706,412

Source: Bureau of the Census.

A glance at the composite picture of specified resources and value of farm products sold by types in table 5-1 reveals an arrangement of characteristics quite different from the orderly progression of the same characteristics for economic classes of farms. This is natural enough because the differences in type are differences in kind rather than in degree as is the case with scale.

TABLE 5-1.—PERCENTAGE OF FARMS, SPECIFIED RESOURCES AND VALUE OF FARM SALES, BY TYPE OF FARM, UNITED STATES, 1950

Type of farm	Number of farms	Land in farms	Value of land and buildings	Expenditure for hired help [1]	Value of farm products sold [1]
	Percent	Percent	Percent	Percent	Percent
All commercial.........	100.0	100.0	100.0	100.0	100.0
Cash-grain...........	11.6	16.9	21.0	8.9	14.5
Cotton..............	16.4	6.5	8.1	18.6	10.2
Other field-crop........	11.0	3.7	5.0	8.3	6.8
Vegetable............	1.3	.5	1.5	5.9	2.3
Fruit-and-nut........	2.2	.8	4.1	9.7	3.4
Dairy..............	16.3	9.5	12.8	13.7	15.5
Poultry.............	4.7	1.2	2.8	2.9	5.5
Livestock [2]	21.8	49.4	30.4	18.1	28.9
General:					
Primarily crop.......	2.3	2.0	2.4	3.2	2.0
Primarily livestock...	3.6	2.2	2.9	1.2	2.6
Crop-and-livestock...	7.4	6.3	7.6	4.1	6.1
Miscellaneous........	1.4	1.0	1.4	5.4	2.2

[1] Data relate to 1949 crop year.
[2] Livestock other than dairy and poultry.

Livestock (other than dairy and poultry) is the most numerous type for the United States followed by cotton, dairy, other field-crop and cash-grain. Vegetable and fruit-and-nut farms have the smallest numbers, except for some of the minor types that are put together in the miscellaneous basket at the end of the classification.

In terms of value of products sold, there was some shifting around in the relative order. Livestock is still first, but next in order are dairy, cash-grain, and cotton. Poultry, vegetable, and fruit-and-nut farms have a higher percentage of total value of products sold than of numbers of farms.

With respect to command over resources, several points may be noted. The very high proportion of land controlled by other livestock farms is related to the extensive ranching operations in the western states. The large wheat farms in the northern and southern plains make cash-grain farms next in percentage of land in farms.

The average characteristics of the several types of farms on a per-farm basis are subject to the usual limitations of averages that cover a variety of conditions, but they are nevertheless revealing (table 5-2).

TABLE 5-2.—SPECIFIED RESOURCES, EXPENDITURE FOR HIRED LABOR, AND VALUE OF FARM SALES; AVERAGE PER FARM, BY TYPE OF FARM; UNITED STATES, 1950

| Type of farm | Farm acreage | | Value of land and buildings | Expenditure for hired labor [1] | Value of farm prod-ucts sold [1] |
	All land	Crop-land			
	Acres	*Acres*	*Dollars*	*Dollars*	*Dollars*
All commercial................	275.6	122.5	17,696	1,009	5,858
Cash-grain..................	401.0	293.1	31,844	723	7,306
Cotton.....................	108.3	69.7	8,690	1,399	3,622
Other field-crop.............	93.1	49.5	7,997	761	3,610
Vegetable..................	116.6	67.9	21,349	4,365	10,838
Fruit-and-nut..............	96.2	54.4	32,918	3,544	8,989
Dairy.....................	161.4	87.8	13,914	806	5,567
Poultry....................	72.6	41.6	10,518	871	6,796
Livestock [2]	625.5	161.9	24,656	791	7,789
General:					
Primarily crop............	247.5	120.7	18,833	1,317	5,220
Primarily livestock........	164.1	101.1	14,174	327	4,226
Crop-and-livestock........	233.1	138.6	17,985	504	4,838
Miscellaneous..............	199.8	50.6	18,552	4,952	9,419

[1] Data relate to 1949 crop year.
[2] Livestock other than dairy and poultry.

Other livestock and cash-grain farms average largest in acres; they are followed by general and miscellaneous farms. But on the basis of value of land and buildings fruit-and-nut farms rank first, followed by cash-grain, other livestock, and vegetable farms. Very high expenditures for hired labor are found on vegetable, fruit-and-nut, and miscellaneous farms. These types have the highest values of products sold, but their heavier expenditures for labor and other items must be kept in mind.

Geographic distribution of types

The concentration or diffusion of the several types and their regional distributions can be more readily seen in the dot maps that follow. The first map shows *cash-grain* farms (fig. 5-3 top). Cash-grain farms are found mainly in the Corn Belt States and the Great Plains. Smaller groups are found in other areas mainly in the West and South. In the Corn Belt cash-grain farm crops are primarily corn and soybeans. In the Plains States they are mainly wheat farms. In other areas they

FIGURE 5-3. CASH-GRAIN FARMS (TOP) AND COTTON FARMS (BOTTOM), NUMBER,
CENSUS OF 1950

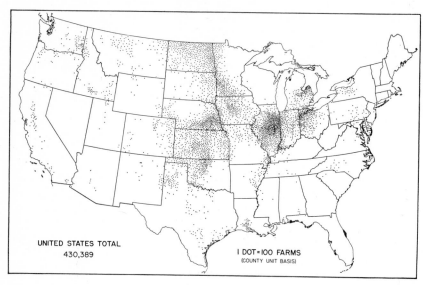

UNITED STATES TOTAL
430,389

I DOT=100 FARMS
(COUNTY UNIT BASIS)

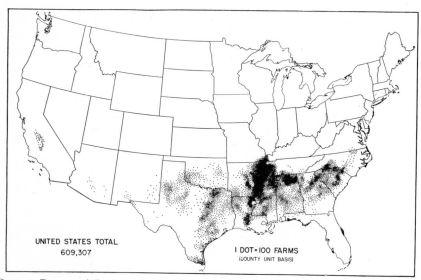

UNITED STATES TOTAL
609,307

I DOT=100 FARMS
(COUNTY UNIT BASIS)

Source: Bureau of the Census.

may be chiefly other combinations of these crops with grain sorghums, small grains, rice, cowpeas, and dry field beans and peas.

Cotton farms were classified on the basis of the one crop; therefore, their location corresponds closely with that of cotton acreage. A broad regional belt of cotton farms extends across the Old South and on west into the irrigated areas of the Southwest and California. Areas of special concentration occur in the eastern Cotton Belt. Irrigated areas do not reflect their full significance on this map. In California, for example, individual cotton farms are relatively large in acreage and have very high yields, but their numbers are small. More cotton is produced under irrigation than one might think from this map of acreage.

Other field-crop farms include farms that raise such diverse things as potatoes, tobacco, sugar beets, sugarcane, peanuts, and other specialty crops (fig. 5-4). Some of them are grown individually and some in combinations. Usually only one or two are grown in an area. The very heavy concentrations in Kentucky, Tennessee, Virginia, and the Carolinas are mainly tobacco farms. In Georgia and Alabama, peanut farms are the main ones in the class. In the western states, sugar beets and potatoes account for many of the other field-crop farms.

Vegetable farms are relatively few in number; they do not show up well on the map with the scale of 1 dot equals 100 farms (fig. 5-5). They are found in localized areas in several parts of the country. The map for value of vegetables harvested for sale shows the localized concentrations somewhat more effectively, although some vegetables are grown on other types of farms as secondary enterprises. Tomatoes, sweet corn, and green peas are frequently produced as such sidelines. Areas of greatest concentration stand out along the Atlantic Seaboard, Florida, lower Rio Grande Valley, Arizona, and California. Important areas are also found in the Lake States and in irrigated intermountain areas in the West.

There are more *fruit-and-nut* than vegetable farms, but their numbers are also few (fig. 5-6). They are somewhat more concentrated in localized areas, as most fruits and nuts grown commercially are closely confined to areas with favorable climates and soils. Citrus fruits, for example, are grown mainly in southern California, Florida, and Texas. The dot map for value of fruits and nuts sold, as in the case of vegetables, shows some areas of commercial fruit-and-nut production not shown on the map of fruit-and-nut farms. They are mainly areas in which fruits and nuts are secondary enterprises in combination types of farming.

Dairy farms are widely diffused over the country, but the principal northern Dairy Belt stands out on the map (fig. 5-7). The sweep of this concentration extends from New England west through Wisconsin

FIGURE 5-4. OTHER FIELD-CROP FARMS (TOP), NUMBER, CENSUS OF 1950; AND PEA-
NUTS GROWN FOR ALL PURPOSES, GROWN ALONE, AND WITH OTHER CROPS (BOTTOM),
ACREAGE, 1949

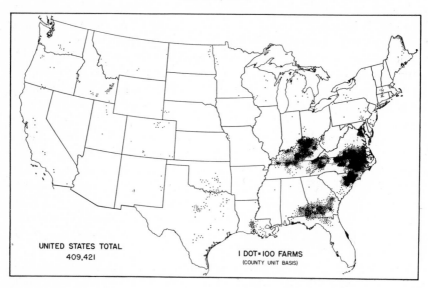

UNITED STATES TOTAL
409,421

1 DOT = 100 FARMS
(COUNTY UNIT BASIS)

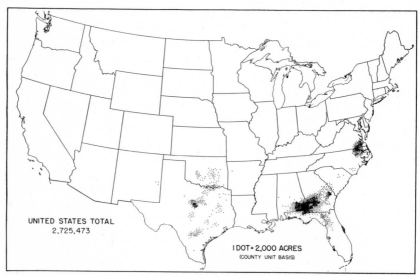

UNITED STATES TOTAL
2,725,473

1 DOT = 2,000 ACRES
(COUNTY UNIT BASIS)

Source: Bureau of the Census.

FIGURE 5-5. VEGETABLE FARMS (TOP), NUMBER, CENSUS OF 1950; AND VALUE OF
VEGETABLES HARVESTED FOR SALE, EXCLUDING IRISH AND SWEET POTATOES (BOTTOM),
DOLLARS, 1949

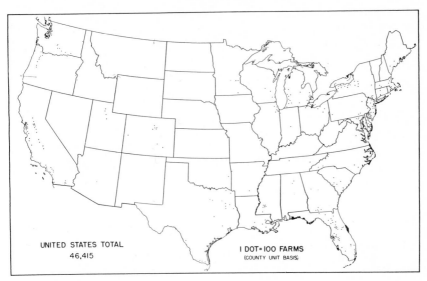

UNITED STATES TOTAL
46,415

I DOT = 100 FARMS
(COUNTY UNIT BASIS)

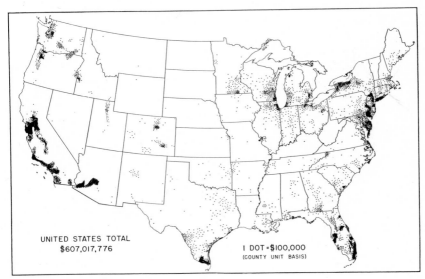

UNITED STATES TOTAL
$607,017,776

I DOT = $100,000
(COUNTY UNIT BASIS)

Source: Bureau of the Census.

FIGURE 5-6. FRUIT-AND-NUT FARMS (TOP), NUMBER, CENSUS OF 1950; AND VALUE
OF FRUITS AND NUTS SOLD (BOTTOM), DOLLARS, 1949

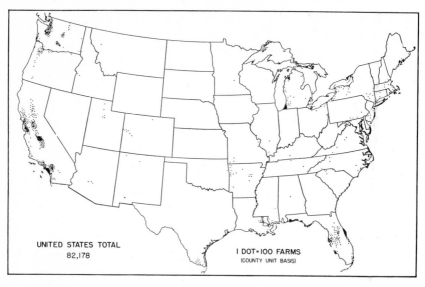

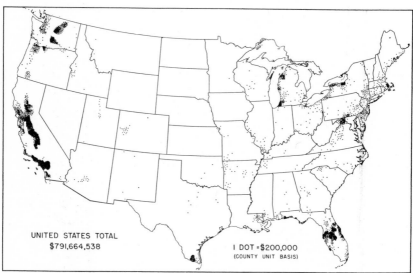

Source: Bureau of the Census.

FIGURE 5-7. DAIRY FARMS (TOP) AND POULTRY FARMS (BOTTOM), NUMBER, CENSUS
OF 1950

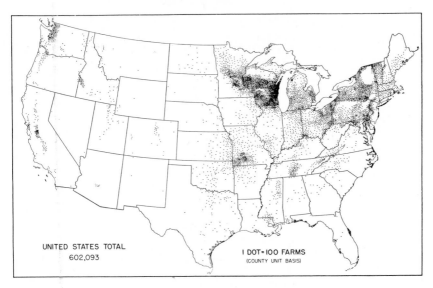

UNITED STATES TOTAL
602,093

I DOT=IOO FARMS
(COUNTY UNIT BASIS)

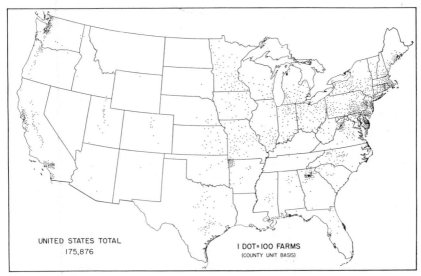

UNITED STATES TOTAL
175,876

I DOT=IOO FARMS
(COUNTY UNIT BASIS)

Source: Bureau of the Census.

and Minnesota. A significant north and south belt of dairying in the Pacific Coast States is also evident. Lesser areas of concentration are found in southwestern Missouri, the Tennessee Central Basin, and some of the western irrigated intermountain valleys.

Availability of pasture and forage and proximity of markets are significant in determining the location of dairy farms. Fluid milk is bulky and perishable, and this increasingly important part of the total milk production shows an urban orientation. As the map shows, the northern Dairy Belt is favorably located with respect to large population centers.

Poultry farms. Production of poultry and poultry products is conducted on specialized poultry farms; it is an important sideline on other types of farms. Although only 3.3 percent of all commercial farms were classified as specialized poultry farms in 1949, 51 percent of commercial farms sold some poultry and eggs. Poultry farms sold about 56 percent of the total value of all poultry and poultry products sold. Production of poultry meat is more in the hands of specialized poultry farmers than is production of eggs. Percentages of all sales are 70 and 40 percent for poultry and eggs, respectively.

The dot map of poultry farms shows that they are most numerous in the Northeast. New Jersey and Delaware, southern New England, and nearby areas especially show up on the map. Scattered clusters in the South and in the Pacific Coast States mark other areas of production. Some of these are centers of commercial broiler production.

Livestock farms, other than poultry and dairy, are more numerous than any other types of farm classified by the 1950 Census (fig. 5-8). Cattle and hogs are produced to some extent in all parts of the country and sheep to a lesser degree. But the western Corn Belt centering on Iowa is the greatest area of production of feed and livestock combined. Indiana and Ohio farther east constitute a secondary center of output. These centers contain the great areas of feeding and fattening hogs, cattle, and sheep.

In the West livestock ranches are more sparsely distributed because available range resources are scattered, but livestock farming is frequently the most important type in an area.

General farms are those that had less than 50 percent of their farm sales from any specified commodity or group of commodities. They form a group that numbers nearly a half million farms which are widely found in all parts of the country, with greater concentrations in areas transitional between more specialized types. For the most part they consist of various combinations of crops and livestock, and for this reason they were subdivided into the three groups on the basis of relative emphasis on crops or livestock.

FIGURE 5-8. LIVESTOCK FARMS, OTHER THAN DAIRY AND POULTRY (TOP), AND GENERAL FARMS (BOTTOM), NUMBER, CENSUS OF 1950

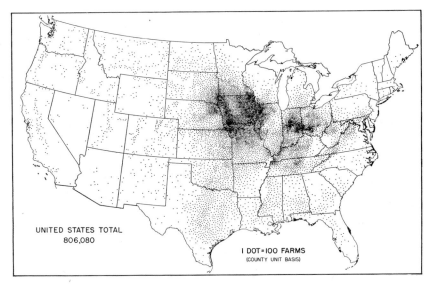

UNITED STATES TOTAL
806,080

I DOT=100 FARMS
(COUNTY UNIT BASIS)

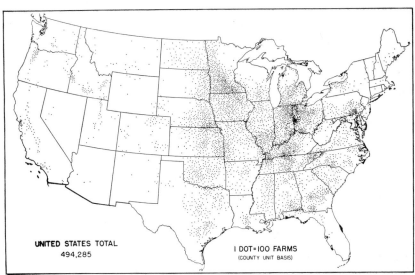

UNITED STATES TOTAL
494,285

I DOT=100 FARMS
(COUNTY UNIT BASIS)

Source: Bureau of the Census.

General farms may be somewhat more flexible and can better adapt to change. Occupying transition positions, with resources that can be turned alternatively to producing different proportions of several commodities, they are strategically situated for meeting changes in economic conditions promptly.

Miscellaneous farms are not shown in a dot map because their numbers are relatively small, they are widely scattered, and they have diverse characteristics. As the name suggests, this group is a miscellaneous collection of many unusual commercial types that were separated from other types in the interest of greater homogeneity. These odd types include forest-product, fur, horticultural, bee, honey, horse, and many other unique types of farms. Each is significant in its own right, but the detail involved does not justify separate handling in a generalized classification. Because of the variety of situations included, statistics for miscellaneous farms are less useful and it is difficult to make even general statements about the group. From table 5-2 it is evident that, on the average, miscellaneous farms have very large investments in land and buildings and that labor hired per farm is highest of any of the twelve types of farms.

Résumé of geography of types. Looking back over the series of dot maps, we can now record some general impressions concerning the geographic distribution of types of farms. Clearly certain types are regionalized. Definite belts or zones mark the location of dairy, cashgrain, cotton, and livestock farms. There is some overlapping, but clear locational patterns are present. Such patterns can be overlaid and joined together in one map as we have seen in the type-of-farming map presented earlier in chapter 3 (fig. 3-9). That map was based upon earlier censuses and upon many detailed federal and state studies of local types of farming.

Using the 1950 Census type classification, the type-of-farming map in fig. 5-2 was constructed on a county-unit basis. Counties were classified into type areas on the basis of the type of farm that constituted 50 percent or more of the commercial farms in each county. One may think of this as a process of overlaying, or stacking, on top of one another a transparent series of the dot maps of types of farms, then marking each county according to the dominant type, provided it accounted for 50 percent or more of all farms.

Any county that had less than 50 percent of its commercial farms in any one type was called *general* and left in white. The very small proportion of the total area of the map in white indicates the relatively high degree of area specialization that characterizes farming in this country. Some *general* farming areas delineate transition areas between zones of greater specialization.

After allowance is made for differences in the definitions of types of farming and in the manner of construction, the map agrees closely with the generalized type-of-farming map shown earlier (fig. 3-9). The broad regional groupings tend to be much the same. Certain limitations of any such generalized presentation are also evident. For example, a state like California which has a diversified combination of types is not well described by this map. California falls mainly in the *general* category, but this covers up the significance of many California types. In recent years, it has been one of the leading states in production of cotton, but the map does not show this. Similarly, less numerous types, like fruit-and-nut, vegetable, and poultry farms, are less than adequately presented on this composite type-of-farming map. No one map can be constructed to show the great variety of farms in a continental nation like ours. Still the nearest approach possible is of considerable aid.

High degree of specialization. The preceding discussion suggests the rather high degree of specialization in one or a few products for sale that characterizes so much of our farming, which differs from the "mixed-farming" type commonly found in many European countries which grows many products. To show this more precisely one may turn to a more specific delineation of certain types of farms (table 5-3). This table lists nineteen selected types of commercial family-operated farms located in major producing areas in widely scattered locations. These selected types represent the most common types in their respective farming areas.

On about three-fourths of the 19 types roughly 50 percent of the cash receipts came from one enterprise, more than 70 percent from two enterprises, and more than 85 percent from three enterprises. Such percentages represent a very high degree of specialization.

Implications of such specialized organizations are important in terms of agricultural adjustment and farm policy. The possibilities of shifting resources between alternative enterprises tend to become limited with specialization. The need for making major adjustments through adopting new technology and by getting the best scale adjustments becomes more significant. When lower prices or other adverse economic factors come over the horizon, costs must be reduced in one way or another.

Interrelationships of economic class and type of farm

Thus far our description of commercial farms has approached economic class and type of farm as separate categories, although interrelationships have frequently been touched upon. Before leaving the subject, a final examination of the economic class composition of commercial farms of each type and of the type composition of commercial

TABLE 5-3.—PROPORTION OF CASH RECEIPTS OBTAINED FROM SALES OF ONE, TWO, AND THREE LEADING ENTERPRISES, 19 AVERAGE COMMERCIAL FAMILY-OPERATED FARMS; SELECTED AREAS; AVERAGE 1947–1949

Type of farm and location	Percentage of receipts from—		
	Leading enterprise	Two leading enterprises	Three leading enterprises
	Percent	*Percent*	*Percen*
Dairy farms:			
Central Northeast................................	78	90	98
Eastern Wisconsin...............................	57	71	85
Western Wisconsin..............................	59	76	87
Corn Belt farms:			
Hog-dairy......................................	45	75	87
Hog-beef-raising...............................	47	76	84
Hog-beef-fattening.............................	53	93	97
Cash-grain.....................................	47	65	75
Tobacco-livestock farms:			
Kentucky bluegrass.............................	67	77	83
Cotton farms:			
Southern Piedmont.............................	64	71	76
Delta of Mississippi............................	85	90	93
Black Prairie, Texas............................	75	84	89
High Plains, Texas (nonirrigated)................	78	90	93
High Plains, Texas (irrigated)...................	84	91	95
Spring-wheat farms (Northern Plains):			
Wheat-small-grain-livestock.....................	52	67	77
Wheat-corn-livestock...........................	21	40	55
Winter-wheat farms:			
Wheat-pea (Washington and Idaho)..............	54	84	88
Sheep ranches:			
Northern Plains................................	83	91	96
Cattle ranches:			
Northern Plains................................	78	91	95
Intermountain region...........................	97	98	98

Source: Computed from data in Agricultural Research Service, "Farm Costs and Returns, 1953 (With Comparisons)." *U. S. Dept. Agr. Inf. Bul. 128*, 1954, and other unpublished data from Production Economics Research Branch, ARS.

farms of each economic class is in order. How are cash-grain farms, for example, distributed among economic classes? And how are large-scale farms distributed among types? What aggregate relationships should we remember?

We can obtain answers to these questions from a two-way table with top headings for economic classes and side headings for types of farms. Both sets of relationships may be seen in one table if we are willing to look at absolute data. But it is more convenient to make two tables showing percentage distributions by vertical columns and horizontal lines (tables 5-4 and 5-5). Percentages in the vertical columns of table 5-4 show the type composition of each economic class, and the percentages read across the horizontal lines in table 5-5 show the economic class composition of each type of farm.

TABLE 5-4.—NUMBER OF COMMERCIAL FARMS, BY ECONOMIC CLASS, AND PERCENTAGE
DISTRIBUTION OF ALL COMMERCIAL FARMS AND OF EACH ECONOMIC CLASS, BY
TYPE OF FARM, UNITED STATES, 1950

Type of farm	Unit	All commercial farms	Economic class					
			Class I	Class II	Class III	Class IV	Class V	Class VI
Number of farms............	Thousands	3,706	103	381	721	882	902	717
Cash-grain................	Percent	11.6	13.3	19.4	17.7	12.4	7.5	5.1
Cotton...................	Percent	16.4	10.9	7.1	6.2	10.4	21.7	33.3
Other field-crop...........	Percent	11.0	4.7	3.4	5.2	13.0	15.9	13.5
Vegetable.................	Percent	1.3	3.0	1.3	0.9	1.0	1.2	1.6
Fruit-and-nut.............	Percent	2.2	5.1	2.9	2.1	2.1	2.2	1.6
Dairy....................	Percent	16.3	9.7	16.1	21.4	20.4	14.8	8.9
Poultry..................	Percent	4.7	8.4	5.9	4.0	3.9	4.8	5.5
Livestock [1]...............	Percent	21.8	35.7	32.3	26.2	20.0	17.0	17.8
General..................	Percent	13.3	5.0	10.1	15.4	15.8	13.5	11.1
Miscellaneous.............	Percent	1.4	4.2	1.5	0.9	1.0	1.4	1.6
Total................	Percent	100.0	100.0	100.0	100.0	100.0	100.0	100.0

[1] Livestock other than dairy and poultry.

TABLE 5-5.—NUMBER OF COMMERCIAL FARMS, BY TYPE OF FARM, AND PERCENTAGE
DISTRIBUTION OF ALL COMMERCIAL FARMS AND OF EACH TYPE OF FARM, BY ECO
NOMIC CLASS, UNITED STATES, 1950

Type of farm	Number of farms	Percentage by economic class						
		Class I	Class II	Class III	Class IV	Class V	Class VI	Total
All commercial farms..........	*Thousands* 3,706	*Percent* 2.8	*Percent* 10.3	*Percent* 19.5	*Percent* 23.8	*Percent* 24.3	*Percent* 19.3	*Percent* 100.0
Cash-grain.........	430	3.2	17.2	29.7	25.5	15.8	8.6	100.0
Cotton.............	609	1.8	4.5	7.4	15.0	32.2	39.1	100.0
Other field-crop...'....	410	1.2	3.2	9.1	27.9	35.0	23.6	100.0
Vegetable..........	47	6.6	10.5	14.5	19.9	23.3	25.2	100.0
Fruit-and-nut........	82	6.4	13.4	18.8	23.0	24.3	14.1	100.0
Dairy..............	602	1.7	10.2	25.6	29.9	22.1	10.5	100.0
Poultry............	176	4.9	12.8	16.2	19.3	24.5	22.3	100.0
Livestock [1].........	806	4.6	15.2	23.5	21.9	18.9	15.9	100.0
General............	494	1.0	7.8	22.4	28.1	24.6	16.1	100.0
Miscellaneous........	50	8.7	11.5	13.1	18.1	25.2	23.4	100.0

[1] Livestock other than dairy and poultry.

Let us look at the vertical columns of table 5-4. Note first the distribution of types for the total of all commercial farms. Livestock is the most numerous type, followed by cotton, dairy, and general. As one examines the relative distributions in each economic class, it is apparent that the most pronounced difference between the higher and lower economic classes lies in the proportion of livestock and of crop types of farming. The higher economic classes have the higher proportions of livestock types, and the lower economic classes the lower proportions. This is less true for each individual type. For example, dairy farms are relatively more important in economic classes III and IV, and cash-grain farms are relatively more numerous in economic class II than elsewhere. The large percentages of cotton and other field-crop farms make these types the leading ones in economic classes V and VI.

As we examine the horizontal-line distributions by types in table 5-5 this can be seen still more closely. More than half of the cash-grain farms fall in economic classes III and IV. But nearly three-fourths of the cotton farms are in economic classes V and VI (the small family-scale and the small-scale farms). Other field-crop farms are also concentrated at the lower end of the economic scale classes.

There are many small vegetable farms and small fruit-and-nut farms. But the percentages of these types that fall in economic class I (large-scale) are higher than those for any other types except miscellaneous. Poultry farms, too, are distributed in much the same way. These three types can be successfully operated in a wider range of sizes. A considerable part of commercial production comes from rather large operations.

Economic classes III and IV are the modal sizes among other livestock farms, but economic class IV is the leading size for general farms.

Significant regional differences in interrelationships between economic classes and types of farms exist. In general, larger proportions of most types of farms in the South fall in the lower economic classes and in the West larger proportions fall in the higher economic classes than is true for the North. If we look at the small-scale farms in economic class VI they appear to be typically dairy, poultry, and other livestock farms in the North, mainly cotton and other field-crop farms in the South, and more widely distributed among five or six leading types in the West. Similar differences are found in other economic classes.

CHAPTER 6

FARM TENURE AND DEBT

Farm tenure and debt relationships are closely interwoven means for bringing together capital resources used in farm production. Tenure and mortgage instruments are results of long evolution through common law and special statute. They are the farmer's substitutes for the stocks and bonds that symbolize corporate business. Because of the limited size of most farm business units, the number of flexible devices for raising venture capital and for borrowing funds is smaller than in urban business. In the past, much of the thought devoted to improving tenure and debt relationships was from the viewpoint of protecting the legal rights of the separate parties involved. Recently more attention has been given to how such relationships may affect efficiency of production and the mutual interests of all concerned.

Farm tenure

Tenure refers to the way in, or the period for, which anything is held or enjoyed. The general concept is not limited to real estate. Problems of tenure may arise with respect to almost any resource used in production (or for that matter in consumption). Human slavery, for example, is a form of tenure exercised over labor, which is no longer tolerated by civilized peoples. A patent or a copyright is a kind of economic tenure granted by the Nation, which gives an individual exclusive rights for a term of years in an invention or a book. An annual service contract between a large-scale wheat grower and a machinery company to repair the wheat grower's tractors, to provide spare parts, and to keep the machines in running order through all emergencies is essentially a form of tenure for the economic services included.

Each business man or farmer continuously brings together resources and services with which to carry on his specific line of production. Most of the time he does not stop to think about tenure problems, because the organizational framework that society has developed minimizes or takes care of many of them automatically. This is one of the principal institutional differences between the self-sufficient types of farming of former times and the commercialized types of the present.

Under our highly competitive system, nearly all the mobile production resources used by farmers are freely available at a price. It is usually unnecessary to establish complete control of the sources from which they come, or even to enter into contracts in order to be sure of access to future flows of these goods and services. Mixed feeds, fertilizers, gasoline, and similar production goods are examples of resources bought and used in relatively short time intervals. The tenure problem may enter in some degree if it is considered desirable to make periodic contracts with particular firms to assure a supply. One may acquire a *right* to be supplied in the event of future shortage. A *base* of good will may be established. Occasionally a farmer may practice some vertical integration by operating several farms or businesses, some of which may supply production materials to the others. A dairyman may also be a feed dealer and supply his own mixed feed. A Corn Belt cattle feeder may have a western cattle ranch on which feeder cattle are raised. A farmer member of a Rural Electrification Administration cooperative may consider this a kind of tenure by means of which he and his fellow cooperators provide their supply of electricity. These examples suggest some of the ways in which tenure in the broad sense affects the control of non-real-estate resources on the farm.

But farm tenure is usually thought of in reference to farm real estate. The rights of individuals to the use of land, buildings, and other fixed capital goods attached to the land are involved. Notice that tenure has two important dimensions. As stated above, "tenure refers to the way in, or the period for, which anything is held" or used. Or to turn it around, one may say that the two significant aspects of farm tenure are the *time period* and the other *rights and conditions* under which farm real estate is held by the operator.

Neither full ownership nor any form of tenancy enables an individual farmer to escape from some part of the network of tenure relationships. No form of tenure allows an operator to do entirely as he pleases with his farm. Except in a one-man Robinson Crusoe economy, other people always have claims to some of the "sticks" in the "bundle of rights" associated with land. Full owners must pay property taxes in recognition of the claims of society. They may be required by law to maintain fences or to eliminate noxious weeds. They may have to accept acreage allotments for particular crops. Their farms may be encumbered with mortgage debt which, though not technically a form of tenure, is closely related to it.

The *time period* is in some ways of greatest consequence in farm tenure. Considerable periods of time are required for completion of many production processes. Long-term capital investments are often necessary for greater efficiency, and time is necessary to recover such investments. An operator does not consider it worth while to increase efficiency in this way unless he is sure that he will be around long enough to benefit from it.

Because the site of the farm home is usually on the farm itself, the lives and well-being of the members of the farm family are also vitally affected by the length of time that they may expect to occupy the same home. Tenure arrangements must therefore be examined not only from the viewpoint of production efficiency but also from that of living conditions. Some forms of tenure also contribute more than others to accumulation of capital, to ascension of the agricultural ladder, and to general community welfare.

The agricultural ladder and inheritance. The term "agricultural ladder" should have some explanation. It has a long history. W. G. Spillman, a leading agricultural scientist of his generation, is usually credited with making the concept famous among professional agricultural workers, but its real origin is lost. The picture presented by the metaphor of the ladder may have suggested itself almost automatically to a people accustomed to endless versions of Horatio Alger success stories. It is a form of "Rags to Riches" or "Log Cabin to White House" adapted to the agricultural scene. In its usual formulation, the successive rungs on the ladder included status as a farm laborer, a tenant, an owner subject to mortgage, and finally an owner free from mortgage debt.

This concept once served to picture the progression by which a young farmer ascended to the economic heaven of ownership. But far-reaching changes in the last quarter century have almost eliminated the agricultural ladder in the old sense. A new agricultural ladder of growing significance has been described as a five-rung process, beginning with 4-H club work and proceeding through apprenticeship, partnership, transfer arrangement, and finally to full ownership.[1] Those who follow this route are usually sons or sons-in-law of established farmers. Obviously there are many different ways of ascending the agricultural ladder.

The legal and customary institutions connected with the transfer of land from one generation to the next are less binding and restrictive here than in most other countries. Land has less prestige value and is less related to status here than elsewhere. These facts have helped to keep a fairly free and open market for land with regular buying and selling in most agricultural areas. Sales of land are at values more nearly related to long-time earning power. All this has meant that the settlement of estates with numerous heirs has interfered less with economic adjustments in use of land than has been true in some countries.

Yet the tangible nature of real estate and the large fixed investment necessary in a going concern mean that a young farmer who is in line

1 Marshall Harris, "A New Agricultural Ladder," *Land Economics*, Aug. 1950, pp. 258-266.

to succeed to a particular farm is in a preferred position. Family ties and relationships are more important in determining who shall become the operator of a particular farm business than is true in urban employment. The son of a city worker may not feel any special interest in the firm for which his father works. He may seek employment in a competing concern if he gets into the same line of business at all. He receives his inheritance by way of a good education and associations in an environment in which opportunities in various fields may develop. When his parents pass on, his formal inheritance, if any, will be in a few impersonal bonds and stock certificates, or in nonbusiness real estate.

Obviously there is a connection between "good farming" and the expectation that a particular farm is likely to be in the family for more than one generation. Some pride of workmanship and personal identification with the soil, as well as the expectation of greater financial returns from careful management, is included in the scope of the over-all relationships. These attributes are associated with the greater permanence and stability of tenure.

Forms of farm tenure.[2] Traditionally, in this country, ownership by the operating farmer is regarded as the most nearly ideal form of tenure. Under American conditions, ownership probably has come closer to the desirable goal than other forms. But in other countries good results have been achieved under certain kinds of tenancy. Security of tenure and other advantages may be more closely related to detailed terms and conditions than to the outward forms of tenure. Investment of limited capital in machinery and equipment may be better for many farmers than ownership of land, and they may thus avoid the risk of a heavy mortgage debt.

Nevertheless, it may be taken as good news that the percentage of all farms operated by tenants in this country was lower in 1950 than at any time since 1880 when tenure data were first collected (table 6-1). Leased farms in 1950 were only 26.8 percent of all farms, or a little more than in 1880, but this was 30 percent below the percentage of tenancy in 1940 (fig. 6-1).

Historical comparisons on tenure matters must be handled carefully because of changes in census procedures and in ways of asking tenure questions. The reported over-all decrease in the percentage of tenancy between 1940 and 1950 was affected by the increase in noncommercial farms which are largely owned and by the decrease in sharecropper farms in the South. Even so, the downward change in the percentage of tenancy has been significant for the main body of commercial farms.

---

2 For a graphic summary of farm tenure see Bureau of the Census, *Farm Tenure, U. S. Census of Agriculture: 1950*, Vol. 5, *Special Report*, Part 5, 1952. (Cooperative with Bureau of Agricultural Economics.)

TABLE 6-1.—PERCENTAGE OF FARMS AND FARMLAND OPERATED BY TENANTS AND OF TOTAL FARMLAND UNDER LEASE, UNITED STATES, 1880 TO 1950

Year	Percentage of total		
	Operated by tenants		Farmland under lease
	Farms	Farmland	
	Percent	Percent	Percent
1880......	25.6	[1]	[1]
1890......	28.4	[1]	[1]
1900......	35.3	23.3	[1]
1910......	37.1	25.8	[1]
1920......	38.1	27.7	[1]
1930......	42.4	31.1	43.7
1940......	38.7	29.4	44.1
1950......	26.8	18.3	35.4

[1] Not available.

Tenure data for 1940 are not separately available for commercial and noncommercial farms, therefore the changes cannot be measured closely. The sharp reduction in percentage of tenancy from 1940 to 1950 is clearly related to the change in the farm income situation from the 1930's to the 1940's.

Nearly half (48.9 percent) of the commercial farms in the United States were operated by full owners in 1950. If part owners are added to full owners, more than two-thirds of all commercial farms were owner operated. Farms operated by tenants made up about 30 percent and those operated by managers something like 0.5 percent (table 6-2). Owner operation is the predominant form of farm tenure in this country. The percentage of all farmland under lease is higher than the percentage of farms operated by tenants, because of the rented land in part-owner farms and the tendency for rented farms to be somewhat larger than owned farms in many areas.

Tenure arrangements assume many detailed forms, and the census classification serves only to set forth some of the broad groups. The accompanying tabulation indicates these tenancy groups and the num-

	Thousand farms
All tenants (commercial)....	1,144
Cash......................	133
Share-cash.................	190
Crop-share.................	347
Livestock-share.............	112
Croppers..................	279
Other.....................	83

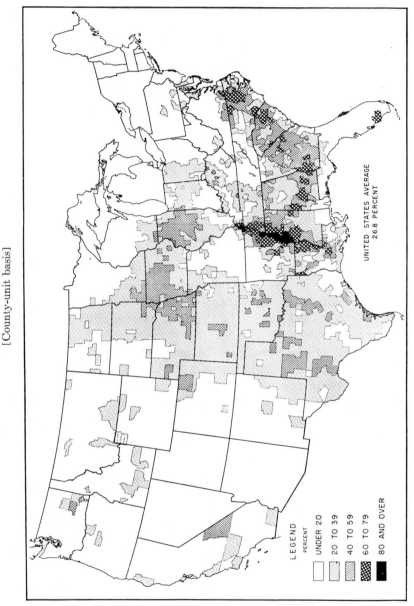

FIGURE 6-1. PERCENTAGE OF ALL FARMS OPERATED BY TENANTS, APRIL 1, 1950

[County-unit basis]

LEGEND
PERCENT

UNDER 20
20 TO 39
40 TO 59
60 TO 79
80 AND OVER

UNITED STATES AVERAGE
26.8 PERCENT

Source: Bureau of the Census.

TABLE **6-2.**—NUMBER OF COMMERCIAL FARMS BY ECONOMIC CLASS OF FARM AND PERCENTAGE OF EACH ECONOMIC CLASS GROUP BY TENURE OF OPERATOR, UNITED STATES, 1950

Economic class	Number of farms	Percentage of farms by tenure of operator				
		Full owners	Part owners	All owners	Managers	Tenants
	Thousands	*Percent*	*Percent*	*Percent*	*Percent*	*Percent*
All commercial farms.....	3,706	48.9	19.7	68.6	0.5	30.9
I.........................	103	36.3	39.0	75.3	6.4	18.3
II.........................	381	37.7	32.1	69.8	1.5	28.7
III.........................	721	43.5	26.1	69.6	0.7	29.7
IV.........................	882	50.0	19.8	69.8	0.2	30.0
V.........................	902	52.8	14.2	67.0	0.1	32.9
VI.........................	717	55.8	10.5	66.3	0.1	33.6

ber of commercial farms in each in 1950. Nearly a third of all commercial tenant farmers operated under a crop-share leasing arrangement, and another 25 percent were croppers. Share leasing in some form was involved in more than 80 percent of the tenant farms.

Tenure and economic class of farm. Comparison of tenure and economic class of commercial farms shows several relationships (table 6-2). In general, the higher the economic class the lower the percentage of farms operated by full owners. A reverse relationship appears for part-owner farms. The percentage of part-owner farms is low in the lower economic classes; it increases as income goes up. But, if full owners and part owners are combined, there is surprisingly little variation between economic classes. That is, there is little correlation between owner-based operations and economic class. Nearly the same statement can be made for aggregate tenancy except that class I (large-scale) farms have a low percentage of tenancy, which is offset partly by a higher than average percentage of managers. Some of the explanation for the difference between full-owner and part-owner situations may be related to the life cycle of the individual operator family, but no doubt other factors, too, are connected.

Tenure and type of farm. The relationship between tenure and type of farm appears to be more definite than that between tenure and economic class (table 6-3). It is evident that the percentage of tenancy runs much higher on crop than on livestock farms. Fruit-and-nut farms appear to represent an exception to this statement, but actually such farms, because of their long-run capital investment in trees, resemble livestock farms more than they do annual-crop farms. Security of

TABLE 6-3.—NUMBER OF COMMERCIAL FARMS BY TYPE OF FARM AND PERCENTAGE
OF EACH TYPE-OF-FARM GROUP BY TENURE OF OPERATOR, UNITED STATES, 1950

Type of farm	Number of farms	Percentage of farms by tenure of operator				
		Full owners	Part owners	All owners	Managers	Tenants
	Thousands	*Percent*	*Percent*	*Percent*	*Percent*	*Percent*
All commercial farms....	3,706	48.9	19.7	68.6	0.5	30.9
Cash-grain................	430	31.6	30.4	62.0	0.3	37.7
Cotton....................	609	25.0	13.1	38.1	0.2	61.7
Other field-crop...........	410	38.7	14.4	53.1	0.2	46.7
Vegetable.................	47	54.1	23.4	77.5	1.0	21.5
Fruit-and-nut..............	82	81.0	9.9	90.9	3.0	6.1
Dairy.....................	602	64.6	19.8	84.4	0.6	15.0
Poultry...................	176	83.2	9.0	92.2	0.5	7.3
Livestock [1]...............	806	55.5	22.6	78.1	0.8	21.1
General...................	494	50.8	23.9	74.7	0.3	25.0
Miscellaneous..............	50	80.9	9.6	90.5	2.1	7.4

[1] Livestock other than dairy and poultry.

tenure for a long period of years is prerequisite to the heavy initial investment and the long waiting time before orchards come into bearing.

Poultry farms also have an especially low rate of tenancy but for different reasons. Here, a relatively small investment in real estate is required, and operating credit for the chief resources is frequently furnished through feed dealers and other financiers.

Management problems both on fruit-and-nut farms and on poultry farms are such that landlords hesitate to invest capital in these ventures and fear to take a chance of getting a tenant who is not a good operator. Failure to spray, prune, and fertilize fruit trees properly at the right time can be disastrous. Similarly, technical knowledge and prompt action in emergencies are essential to success on poultry farms.

Tenure and other relationships. Length of occupancy on a given farm is important from the viewpoint of production efficiency and also because of its bearing on the life of the farm family. Average length of occupancy for farm operators in different tenure groups in 1950 gives some impression of this factor. The average periods are given in the accompanying tabulation. These periods represent the average length

All operators.	13 years
Full owners....	16 years
Part owners...	14 years
Tenants.......	6 years

of time on the same farm for operators according to their 1950 tenure status. In some cases they may have been climbing the agricultural ladder on the same farm for longer periods.

Kinship between landlord and tenant must be taken into account in understanding tenancy. In 1950, more than one-fifth (21.7 percent) of all tenants in the United States were close relatives of their landlords. Under census instructions this meant that the landlord was a parent, grandparent, brother, or sister of the operator or his wife. In the Northeast and the North Central States nearly a third of all tenants were close kin.

Significance of the tenure structure. A few general statements can be made about the significance of farm-tenure structure. Perhaps the main point is that the intangible details and conditions are frequently of greater consequence than the formal outward structure. We are impressed by the fact that the percentage of tenancy has decreased in recent years, but such things as debt reduction for owner operators and progress in devising more equitable landlord-tenant leases to fit conditions in each region and area may be more significant.

Other things being equal, farmers in a debt-free full-owner classification have the most flexibility in combining their resources to maximize efficiency and income over time. A debt-free owner has the greatest amount of freedom and of security, the most certain tenure, and his family enjoys many living advantages. This may be a farm operator's lifetime goal. But, as in many other situations, an ultimate goal may not be the best form of tenure for young operators, operators with limited experience, those with small capital, or those with many of the other limitations that are likely to be present among any normal group of farm operators. In fact, it may not be the best ultimate goal for many individuals in view of all considerations and sacrifices that may be entailed. The various forms of tenancy and credit arrangements are methods that have been devised to cope with such situations. Used properly, with the right safeguards, they can offset limitations and bring together resources and managerial ability, join experience with inexperience, and further the interests of all individuals concerned.

Forms of debt and tenure are sometimes blamed as causes when they are only indicators or symptoms of economic distress. They may have been the best means available for meeting the situation that prevailed at the time. But it is true that, once established, tenure patterns may be continued beyond their time and place of usefulness.

Because of the high percentage of short-term tenancy in annual-crop types of farming, many questions arise concerning the relation between tenure and conservation. A tenant operator frequently must place a high premium on early returns, and his cropping program may therefore be exploitive. How far he goes in this direction depends on the kind of lease he has. A share lease, with both costs and returns shared, will reduce his risks. The way in which variable costs like fertilizer are shared will affect rates of application and the efficiency of operations.

Hired-management farming. "Corporation, chain, and contract farming," and "commercial farm-management services" are some of the terms used to describe various kinds of hired-management tenure. Not all of them are included under the census heading of farms operated by managers. Hired-manager-operated farms include many that do not differ much from those operated by tenants. It might be difficult to decide whether a manager who is operating under an agreement to share in the profits is a manager or really a tenant. Hobby farms managed for wealthy owners are also covered in the census category of managed commercial farms.

Corporation farming. The 0.5 percent of all commercial farms and the 6.6 percent of commercial farmland operated by hired managers thus included many more farms and much more farmland than were operated as corporation farms. Information on corporation farms is not readily available. The 1950 Census obtained some data on types of owners, which reveal some facts about corporate *ownership* of farmland though little about corporate *operation*.[3] The 1950 distribution of all farmland in the country by ownership is given in the accompanying tabulation.

	Percent
Individual, partnership, or estate....	87.8
Corporation......................	4.4
Indian..........................	3.6
Public..........................	4.2
Total farmland..................	100.0

If we assume that farmland in corporate ownership was nearly all in commercial farms, the 4.4 percent of all farmland would mean about 5 percent of farmland in commercial farms under corporate ownership.

Corporate holdings were most common in the western states and in Florida. Hired managers operated much of the land, especially in ranching and in fruits and vegetables. Farming and ranching companies owned 2.2 percent of the farmland in 1950. Holdings of companies of this type are numerous in Florida and California. Large acreages are devoted to fruits, vegetables, cotton, sugarcane, and grazing. Ranching companies were found throughout the western states. Other corporations, with primary interests in real estate, timber, minerals, and railroads, owned almost 2 percent of the farmland. These corporations seldom farm the land they own; usually they lease it to others for farming and ranching.

In the eastern states most of the relatively small acreage of corporate land in farms is held by industrial companies. They may hold

---

3 Buis T. Inman and Hilton E. Robison, "Changes in Farm Land Ownership," *Agricultural Economics Research*, Oct. 1953, pp. 87–94.

the land for minerals, timber, future factory sites, or other reasons. Few of these companies operate farms.

Chain farming. Some large-scale farms are organized as chain farms. That is, a series of farms under the same ownership (usually corporate) is operated with some unity in overhead management but with a hired manager or tenant in charge of each unit. A chain-farm system differs from a multiple-unit plantation in that it has greater geographic separation and greater autonomy of separate farm units. The farms in the chain may be in the same general locality or the farms may be widely separated. At least one large Texas cattle ranch owns several farms in the Northeast for the purpose of finishing fat cattle for eastern markets. This is an example of vertical integration. Some large commercial potato growers operate several farms under one overhead management. Sometimes they move machinery and labor from one farm to another in succession. This kind of chain operation may be termed horizontal integration.

Contract farming. Contract farming appears in various places with enterprises like sugar beets or canning crops, where it is important for processors to have an assured supply of raw material. Contracts take many forms; the processing company goes so far in some instances as to prepare the land, supply the seed, and harvest the crop.

Commercial farm-management services. A number of commercial farm-management services have arisen, especially in the Corn Belt and the far west. Some of these services grew out of original sponsorship by state agricultural colleges; others arose independently. Services supplied range from regular news letters that contain timely production and marketing advice, through specialized accounting services, to complete management and operation of farms. Some farm-management services specialize in drawing up long-term plans for reorganization of farms rather than in current operations.

Commercial farm-management services are used both by institutions and by individuals with farm investments, who lack the specialized knowledge or the time to supervise tenants or individual managers.

Farm-mortgage debt and non-real-estate loans [4]

A creditor has an equity in the farm business just as has an owner or a tenant. Fractional interests belonging to creditors are shown by the farm-debt structure. Usually mortgage debt secured by farm real estate is a larger item than other debt not only on the individual farm but also in the aggregate. In the last few years, however, total non-real-estate debt has risen to a higher level than mortgage debt. In

---

4 For a recent summary of farm-mortgage data see the special report by the Bureau of the Census, *Farm-Mortgage Debt, U. S. Census of Agriculture: 1950*, Vol. 5, *Special Report*, Part 8, 1952. (Cooperative with Bureau of Agricultural Economics.)

1950, for example, total farm-mortgage debt amounted to $5.6 billion as compared with total non-real-estate debt of about $6.9 billion.

Trends in the two classes of farm debt from 1910 to 1953 are shown in figs. 6-2 and 6-3. Total non-real-estate farm loans include loans and book credits by miscellaneous lenders and Commodity Credit Corporation price-support loans not shown in fig. 6-3.[5] These additional items were estimated to amount to about $4.1 billion in 1950, or more

FIGURE 6-2. FARM-MORTGAGE DEBT HELD BY MAJOR LENDERS

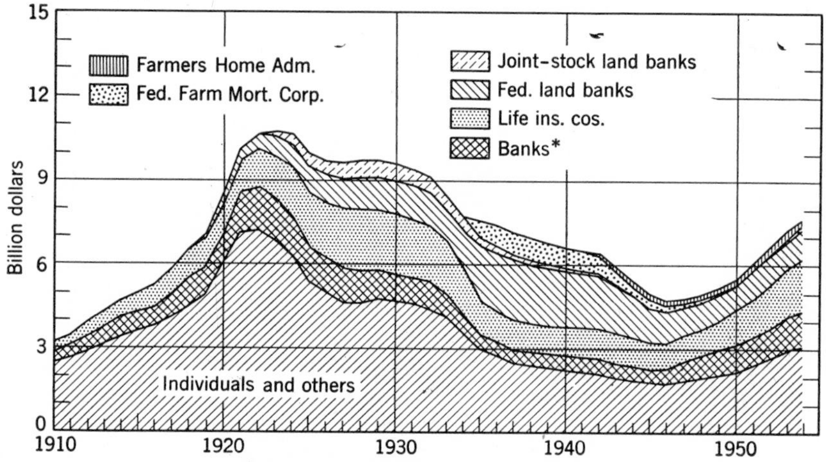

*1910-34, open state and national banks;
1935-47, insured commercial banks;
1948-53, all operating banks.

Source: Agricultural Research Service.

than the $2.8 billion of loans held by banks and federally sponsored agencies shown in the chart.

Distribution of farm-mortgage debt among major lenders indicates that in recent years more than half of the debt has been held by institutional lenders, principally life-insurance companies, commercial banks, and federal land banks. From 1910 to 1920, the greater part was held by individuals and others.

As would be expected, the commercial banking system supplies a much larger proportion of non-real-estate than of mortgage loans. If Commodity Credit Corporation price-support loans are included, the division of non-real-estate loans in 1950 was about as given in the accompanying tabulation.

---

[5] Commodity Credit Corporation price-support loans are nonrecourse loans (without recourse to the borrower). The Commodity Credit Corporation will accept the commodity as settlement of the obligation if the price goes down, and then the borrower does not have to pay the loan in cash. For this reason they are usually listed separately from the more conventional types of credit.

Percent

Commodity Credit Corporation...........	25
Banks and federally sponsored agencies.....	40
Miscellaneous loans and book credits.......	35
Total.............................	100

From the viewpoint of freedom to make managerial decisions, owner-operated farms free from debt are in the most flexible position. In 1950, 71 percent of all full-owner-operated farms were free from mort-

FIGURE 6-3. NON-REAL-ESTATE FARM LOANS HELD BY BANKS AND FEDERALLY SPONSORED AGENCIES

[January 1 and July 1 data; excludes loans held or guaranteed by Commodity Credit Corporation]

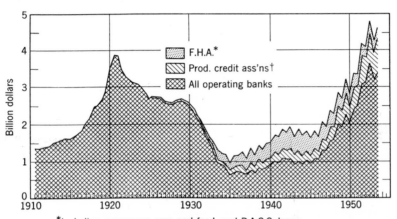

*Including emergency crop and feed, and R.A.C.C. loans.
†Including federal intermediate credit bank discounts for other lenders.

Source: Agricultural Research Service.

gage debt, as compared with 59 percent in 1940 (table 6-4). Corresponding data for part owners were 66 percent in 1950 and 45 percent in 1940. Tenant- and hired-manager-operated farms were nearly 80

TABLE 6-4.—PERCENTAGE OF ALL FARMS FREE FROM MORTGAGE DEBT BY TENURE OF OPERATOR, UNITED STATES, 1940 AND 1950

Tenure of operator	1940	1950
	Percent	*Percent*
All farms...............	61.2	72.5
Full owners...............	58.6	71.1
Part owners...............	45.3	65.9
Tenants and managers......	68.8	79.2

percent free of mortgage debt in 1950, but the burden of real-estate debt in this group does not fall directly on the farm operator.

Average mortgage debt per mortgaged farm rose from $2,786 in 1940 to $3,769 in 1950. But farm values increased even more than debt, therefore the ratio of debt to value for encumbered farms dropped from 42 percent in 1940 to 25 percent in 1950.

The burden of mortgage debt consists not only in the size of the principal that must be repaid but also in the interest charges that must be met. The annual interest burden is considerably less than formerly because of lower interest rates. Average rates of interest on farm-mortgage debt reported by the census for selected years were as tabulated.

Year	Percent
1930	6.0
1935	5.5
1940	4.6
1945	4.5
1950	4.5

In 1950, interest amounted to $169 per mortgaged farm or $0.82 per acre of land in mortgaged farms. This charge is a fourth less than it would have been with 1930 rates of interest.

In summary, nearly three-fourths of all farms in the country were free of mortgage debt in 1950. Those that were encumbered carried a smaller burden than in earlier years, both in terms of the percentage of total value mortgaged and in terms of interest rates paid.

Interrelationships between farm-mortgage debt and tenure in 1950 are further suggested by table 6-5. The percentage of farms mort-

TABLE 6-5.—SELECTED FARM-MORTGAGE MEASURES, BY TENURE OF OPERATOR, UNITED STATES, 1950

| Tenure of operator | Percentage of total | | |
	Farms mortgaged	Farmland in mortgaged farms	Farm value [1] mortgaged
	Percent	Percent	Percent
All farms	27.5	26.2	25.3
Full owners	28.9	32.3	27.6
Part owners [2]	34.1	39.5	25.7
Tenants and managers [3]	20.8	15.3	20.7

[1] On mortgaged farms.
[2] Acres and value for owned portion only.
[3] Acres and value include rented portions of part-owner farms.

gaged is highest among part owners. This is related to age of operator and the time he has had for accumulating capital. Tenant- and manager-operated farms have the lowest percentage encumbered by mortgage. Such farms are more often owned by people who have inherited or accumulated substantial savings. Similar relationships hold for percentage of all farmland and for percentage of the total value of land and buildings in mortgaged farms.

The ratio of debt to value of mortgaged farms is slightly higher for full-owner than for tenant- and manager-operated farms. Here again, the reasons probably relate to general financial status.

CHAPTER 7

PART-TIME AND RESIDENTIAL FARMS

In this chapter we turn from "commercial" to "noncommercial" farms. Noncommercial farms include three groups—part-time, residential, and unusual farms.[1] The considerable numbers and the nonagricultural orientation of noncommercial farms are emphasized by the accompanying tabulated data.

	Number of farms	Percentage of all farms	Percentage of value of all farm products sold
	Thousands	*Percent*	*Percent*
Part-time................	639	11.9	1.7
Residential..............	1,030	19.1	0.4
Unusual.................	4	0.1	0.4
Total noncommercial......	1,673	31.1	2.5

Let us first dispose of the unusual noncommercial farms. These farms are quite unlike part-time and residential farms; they represent unusual types of special-purpose farms. They consist of public and private institutional farms, experimental farms, grazing associations, cooperative farms, community-project farms, Indian reservations, and other unique farms. These unusual farms make up only 0.1 percent of all farms and account for 0.4 percent of the value of all farm products sold. Some individual units are very large. They might have been included among commercial farms except that the purposes they serve differ widely from those of either commercial or part-time and residential farms. Ordinarily unusual noncommercial farms are not operated by individual farmers for income from sale of farm products or as homes for their families. Primary products of many of these special-purpose farms are other services. An experimental farm produces research results; a grazing association supplies feed to member farmers; an institutional farm furnishes food, exercise, and vocational training for some of its inmates. Indian reservations and cooperative or community farm projects represent different forms of economic organization that cannot readily be added in with typical commercial farms. Obviously, many

---

[1] The 1950 Census of Agriculture uses the term "other farms" for "noncommercial farms" and "abnormal farms" for "unusual noncommercial farms." The terms "noncommercial" and "unusual" seem more appropriate and are used in this book.

unusual farms contribute important services to the economy and would be worth study for their own sake. But from the viewpoint of describing agriculture as a whole they can be largely disregarded, as both their numbers and their direct contribution to farm production are negligible.

This chapter is mainly concerned with the one million residential farms and the two-thirds of a million part-time farms. Together they comprise nearly a third of all census-enumerated farms. But with only 2.1 percent of the value of all farm products sold, they do not loom very high on the farm-production horizon. Even the combined values of products produced for sale and for home use probably would not rise above 4 percent, if one may judge from findings based on the 1945 census (home use was not obtained in 1950). The significance of part-time and residential farms therefore does not lie in their contribution to farm production but in the people who live on them and in their other economic activities. The real value of such places as homes will transcend any agricultural values.

Historical origins

Part-time and residential farming in the broad generic sense has always been present to some extent. From ancient times those who "live by the sea" or by seasonal or intermittent occupations, such as lumbering, mining, and fishing, have operated small farms. Historically, certain combinations of farming and early manufacturing, or "cottage industries," were basic links in the chain of industrial evolution.

But the barrier of space and the lack of rapid transportation for workers effectively limited the extent of part-time farming in this country until the advent of automobiles and modern highways. Before World War I only a few research studies were devoted to this problem. It was not until the 1930's that the growth of part-time farming was generally recognized and appreciated. A pioneering analysis of a town in Massachusetts by Rozman was published in 1930.[2] It was a spark that touched off a chain reaction of research and thinking. Rozman sought to explore the possibilities of providing more adequate living by combining urban work with a farm anchor of security against unemployment and financial adversity.

As pointed out in Chapter 4, numbers of part-time and residential farms increased by perhaps two-thirds from 1930 to 1950. At the same time numbers of commercial farms decreased by 30 percent. These opposite trends were not entirely unrelated. Some farms passed from the commercial to the noncommercial category because favorable work alternatives off the farm became available. Fundamentally, the upward trend in numbers of part-time and residential farms is a phase of the

2 David Rozman, "Part-Time Farming in Massachusetts," *Mass. Agr. Expt. Sta. Bul. 266*, 1930.

far-reaching economic and social changes brought about by the impact of modern technology. Automobiles and all-weather roads are the immediate key elements. Improved transportation has so diminished travel time as to enlarge many times the effective area within which people consider it feasible to commute to work. In geometric language the area served by faster transportation increases by the square of the additional radial distance brought within reach. The result has been an increasing intermingling of farm and urban occupations. In the old days a farmer who felt the gravitational attraction of city opportunities pulled up his stakes and moved to the city. Now he may drive his car back and forth and leave the stakes in place.

The visible outward thrust from crowded urban communities, especially since the end of World War II, is another part of the total picture. The amazing peripheral growth of nearly all cities has spilled over into the open country beyond the suburbs and has dotted the landscape with new residences. Some of them have become part-time and residential farms.

Not all this shift in ways of living and working is revealed by the agricultural census. The census definition of a farm leaves out all rural residences that do not produce the minimum of farm products. Many of them differ little from the residential farms that are included.

Definitions

By definition, the 1950 Census part-time farms are those with gross sales of farm products between $250 and $1,199, provided the farm operator reported 100 or more days' work off the farm in 1949, or provided the nonfarm income received by him and members of his family was more than the value of farm products sold. This farm income range is the same as that for the small-scale, class VI, farms. The difference lies in the added provisions concerning off-farm work and income. Part-time farms are thus in a better financial position than small-scale farms.

Residential farms were classified on the sole upper criterion of less than $250 worth of farm products sold. A lower limit was set by the minimums in the definition of a census farm (3 acres or more of land and not less than $150 value of farm products *produced* or if less than 3 acres at least $150 worth of farm products *sold*). Confined within these close statistical walls, residential farms are essentially just what the name implies, homes in the country with a little farm produce raised. Only 65 percent of the residential farms sold any farm products. The other 35 percent produced only for home use.

Part-time and residential farms are defined in the exact terms indicated above, but one should remember that these are arbitrarily imposed definitions. No such sharp distinctions hold in real life; many people, including those who work closely with the data, may have in mind a quite different concept of part-time or residential farming.

Part-time farming in a broader view is practiced clear across the income board. To cut it off at $1,199 is to present a truncated distribution of part-time farms in this generic sense. This is illustrated by the accompanying tabulation, which shows the percentages of operator-

Economic class	Number of farms	Percentage with nonfarm income exceeding farm sales [1]
	Thousands	Percent
All commercial farms........	3,706	9.1
Class I.................	103	4.6
Class II................	381	4.2
Class III..............	721	5.3
Class IV...............	882	10.2
Class V................	902	20.7
Class VI...............	717	—
All noncommercial farms....	1,673	73.6
Part-time..............	639	86.2
Residential............	1,030	65.9
Unusual...............	4	23.7

[1] From data obtained in response to the 1950 Census question, "Was the income which you and your family received from work off the farm and from other sources . . . greater than the total value of all agricultural products sold from your place last year?"

families in each economic class who receive more income from nonfarm sources than they do from sales of farm products.

Most classes of farms contain substantial numbers in which nonfarm income exceeds that from sales of farm products. The small-scale, class VI, group has no such farms because by definition they have been partitioned over into the part-time class.[3] That circumstance in turn accounts for the very high percentage of part-time farms with most of their income from off-farm sources. Therefore, when we deal with part-time farms, under the census definition, we have not covered all farms that might be included under other definitions or analytical approaches. The 21 percent of farms in class V or the 10 percent in class IV could be very important in an analysis of part-time farming. Similar remarks concerning the cutoff of residential farms are pertinent on occasion. It is well to remind ourselves that definitions of many terms are garments of convenience and necessity and that they are subject to change on short notice.

Geographic distribution

Examination of the dot maps of part-time and residential farms indicates areas of concentration of such farms (figs. 7-1 and 7-2). The

[3] Any farm in the class VI income bracket ($250 to $1,199) with nonfarm income in excess of farm sales is a part-time farm.

FIGURE 7-1. PART-TIME FARMS, NUMBER, APRIL 1, 1950

[Farms with gross sales of $250 to $1,199, farm products minor source of income.
Operator working off farm 100 or more days and/or family income from other
sources greater than sales from farm products]

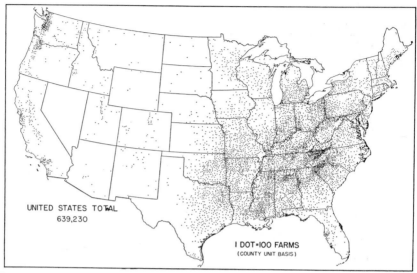

UNITED STATES TOTAL
639,230

I DOT=100 FARMS
(COUNTY UNIT BASIS)

Source: Bureau of the Census.

FIGURE 7-2. RESIDENTIAL FARMS, NUMBER, APRIL 1, 1950

[Farms with gross sales less than $250]

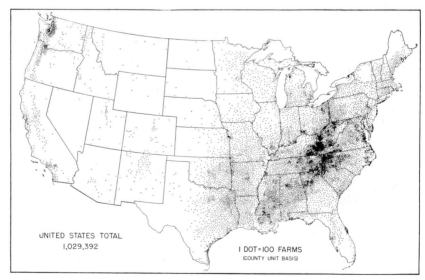

UNITED STATES TOTAL
1,029,392

I DOT=100 FARMS
(COUNTY UNIT BASIS)

Source: Bureau of the Census.

map in fig. 7-3, which shows part-time and residential farms combined as a percentage of all farms, needs to be examined at the same time to get the relative picture. These farms are more numerous in the South than elsewhere. Residential farms have particularly heavy concentrations in the Appalachian areas of West Virginia, eastern Kentucky, and western North Carolina. One might expect to find heavier concentrations of these farms near the larger metropolitan centers, but they do

FIGURE 7-3. PART-TIME AND RESIDENTIAL FARMS AS A PERCENTAGE OF ALL FARMS, 1950

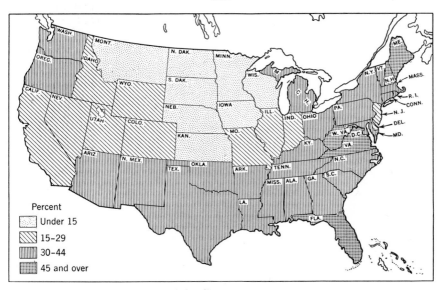

Source: Data are from Bureau of the Census.

not seem especially noticeable. Conditions conducive to part-time and residential farming probably prevail around smaller cities and towns. Hence the phenomenon is well diffused. Another part of the explanation may be that the suburban fringes around the larger metropolitan centers become primarily residential and have so little farm production that they fall outside the farm classification.

The maps suggest also the diverse composition of part-time and residential farming. Those who reach out from cities to find suitable rural living environments have different motives and backgrounds from those who reach in from the country to find employment. Again the occupational relationship in certain areas involves less of the farm-city relationship and more of the farm-mining, farm-lumbering, etc., relationships. Many West Virginia and Kentucky coal miners, for example, combine small farming with intermittent mining operations.

Large numbers of part-time and residential farms in the South are related to the land-tenure systems and to the historical concentration of population in the region. In time, as population in these areas acquires the means and education requisite to mobility, the number of such small farms may also diminish. But one should remember that part-time farming has been maintained in the Northeast and has actually expanded in many areas at the same time that commercial farming has retreated.

In the northern part of the Lake States, part-time and residential farming is interwoven with lumbering and recreational occupations. In each area, historical explanations can be found for the existing situation.

Family and income characteristics

A few references to data characterizing part-time and residential farms appeared in earlier chapters. Average sales of farm products per farm as compared with sales from small-scale commercial farms in 1949 are given in the accompanying tabulation. But information limited to

Small-scale..... $720
Part-time...... 612
Residential.... 82

the agricultural part of the business is likely to be misleading. Analysis of data from the Bureau of Agricultural Economics enumerative survey of 1947 throws additional light on the characteristics of these farms.[4] When account is taken of income from off-farm sources, residential and part-time farms are seen to be in considerably better financial status than small-scale commercial farms. Total gross income per farm was approximately $2,200 and $3,100 for residential and part-time farms, respectively, as compared with less than $800 for small-scale farms (table 7-1). Nearly 60 percent of the residential and 75 percent of the part-time farms in this study reported gross family income of $1,500 and more from all sources. This contrasts with only 5 percent for small-scale farms. The number of persons of working age (14 to 64) was somewhat greater on part-time and residential farms than on small-scale farms (table 7-2). Small-scale farms were occupied by smaller families.

Sources of off-farm income found in the 1947 survey for part-time and residential farms were varied (table 7-3). In nearly 90 percent of the cases the operator reported some off-farm earnings; in about 10 percent, the earnings were by family members only. Civilian wages were the chief source of outside income, but net rents from property, veteran's payments, social security, receipts from boarders, and other businesses were all significant. Residential farms included more re-

---

4 About 4,400 schedules from this survey were analyzed. Certain adjustments for value intervals and price changes were made to conform with the 1950 Census. See Jackson V. McElveen and Kenneth L. Bachman, "Low Production Farms," *U. S. Dept. Agr. Inf. Bul. 108*, June 1953.

TABLE 7-1.—FARM AND NONFARM INCOMES OF OPERATOR AND FAMILY MEMBERS, CLASSIFIED AS RESIDENTIAL, PART-TIME, AND SMALL-SCALE FARMS, UNITED STATES, 1946

Item	Unit	Residential [1]	Part-time [2]	Small-scale [3]
Total gross income per farm	Dollars	2,187	3,076	772
Off-farm income per farm	Dollars	2,000	2,553	112
Farm income per farm	Dollars	187	523	660
Farms reporting gross income, all sources:				
Under $1,000	Percent	27	12	74
$1,000–1,499	Percent	14	14	21
$1,500 and over	Percent	59	74	5
Farms reporting off-farm income:				
Under $1,000	Percent	42	22	100
$1,000 and over	Percent	58	78	—
Percentage of farms reporting any off-farm income	Percent	86	100	44

NOTE.—Based on an analysis of 4,400 schedules from BAE enumerative survey made in 1947 for the preceding year. Cash farm receipts were not adjusted for inventory changes or underreporting. Farms with insufficient data and farms apparently not meeting 1950 census definitions of a farm were excluded.

[1] Under $225 value of sales in 1946.
[2] Farms having value of sales from $225 to $1,099 in 1946, with other income exceeding farm sales.
[3] Farms having value of sales from $225 to $1,099 in 1946, with farm sales exceeding off-farm income.

TABLE 7-2.—PERSONS IN FARM-OPERATOR HOUSEHOLDS BY AGE AND SEX, AND GROSS INCOME PER PERSON OF WORKING AGE, AVERAGES FOR SELECTED ECONOMIC CLASSES OF FARMS, UNITED STATES, 1946

Selected economic class	Average per farm			Gross income per person of working age
	Persons in farm operator households			
	Total	Persons of working age [1]		
		Total	Males	
	Number	Number	Number	Dollars
Small-scale farms	3.9	2.2	1.1	356
Part-time farms	4.4	2.8	1.5	1,090
Residential farms	4.1	2.5	1.2	857

See NOTE, table 7–1.
[1] Persons on farms between the ages of 14 and 64.

TABLE 7-3.—PERCENTAGE OF FARMS REPORTING SPECIFIED SOURCES OF OFF-FARM INCOME, PART-TIME AND RESIDENTIAL FARMS, UNITED STATES, 1946

Item	Percentage of farms reporting	
	Part-time farms	Residential farms
	Percent	*Percent*
Farms reporting off-farm income by:		
Operator only	50	60
Both the operator and one or more family members	38	32
Family members only	12	8
Specified sources of operators' off-farm income:		
Civilian wages	59	57
Net rent from property	16	8
Veteran's payments	12	8
Social security	8	12
Business receipts	8	8
Net income from boarders	5	5

See NOTE, table 7-1.

tired persons. Some farms were home places of landlords with their land rented out, some were training units for veterans. About 14 percent of the operators of residential farms reported no off-farm income at all. These families may have been living on earnings from earlier years and on an extreme subsistence basis.

The percentages of farm operators more than 65 years old on these small farms, as shown by the 1950 Census, are given in the accompanying tabulation. The percentage of 13.6 for part-time farms is close to

	Percent
Small-scale	23.6
Part-time	13.6
Residential	22.0

the average of 13.0 percent for all commercial farms. The larger percentages on both small-scale and residential farms stress the retirement aspect and the apparently more fortunate situation of those on residential farms.

Problems of part-time and residential farms

Many questions can be raised about part-time and residential farms, and additional research is needed before these questions can be answered. How much of the upward trend in recent years in numbers of such farms represents a transitional phase? How much is likely to persist?

With the continued increase in efficiency of commercial farming, is it likely that part-time farming will become less remunerative? Would it represent greater social efficiency to encourage further expansion in part-time farming or to encourage workers to seek full-time off-farm jobs? Surely social efficiency will not be independent of what families themselves wish to do. What may well be encouraged is an expansion of employment opportunities and of living alternatives, leaving people with more freedom to make their own choices.

One should not forget that part-time and residential farms are primarily homes rather than businesses. The greater social and economic values to be considered are not those that can be directly measured by money. Early part-time farming arose as a means of supplementing income from farms that had become too small to provide an acceptable living. Some people have become part-time farmers by finding small farms near nonfarm jobs, to add to inadequate nonfarm earnings, to increase savings, or to escape high urban rents and other expenses. In a number of areas in the Northeast, factory employees migrating from farm backgrounds in other regions wanted to live on small farms. Another reason for part-time and residential farms, although it does not overlook the financial advantages, comes mainly from an interest in rural living, a desire for space, air, sunlight, and outdoor life, and a chance to work with living things.

Although the opportunity for supplementary income is likely to remain a factor in part-time farming, the real living values involved in the last group of reasons may become more compelling. In residential farming they are paramount. Many families who do not need to supplement their money income are interested in part-time or residential farming. They want to get away from overcrowded city life and have a quieter place for the children where they can learn to participate more in family activities. This phase of part-time and residential farming is an important element in the synthesis of urban and rural ways of life that is going on in our current culture. Not all people enjoy country living, but, for those who do, it offers opportunities for a more balanced and less artificial existence. There is reason to believe that more people will avail themselves of these advantages as time goes on. The development of interest in this direction is reinforced by the increasing public concern about the problem of conservation. Conservation of natural resources in terms of soil, water, forests, wildlife, and the like, leads to concern about human resources and living. If enjoyment of the open air and sunshine is a good thing in a national park on vacation, wouldn't many of us enjoy living and working in an environment that would include more space and sunshine than cities now afford?

Thus motives for part-time and residential farming are likely to be mixed. Economic necessity, free choice on the part of those with plentiful resources, the desire to escape urban restrictions, and many other reasons enter. Some, like the fictional Mr. Blanding, have found that the fuller life on the idyllic plane failed to materialize when coupled with a regular 8-hour day in the city. Complete utilization of marginal morning and evening daylight, together with week ends, may destroy more than it builds. Working in the city and living in the country may have both advantages and disadvantages. But people should have the opportunity to make choices with reasonably good understanding of what their choices will entail.

C H A P T E R   8

GROUP INTERESTS IN AGRICULTURE [1]

If James Watt, the eighteenth-century inventor of the steam engine, were to visit a present-day factory, he would find it difficult to understand much of what was going on. He would be puzzled by the many ways of transmitting mechanical power. His contemporary, Adam Smith, would be less bewildered. In fact, if he were to join a conference of fellow economists he would even find some of them trying to explain current economic events in terms of the model that he himself designed in 1776. In his famous book, *The Wealth of Nations,* Adam Smith visualized a competitive model in a general framework of moral sentiment and law that fitted the circumstances of an England rapidly emerging from regulated feudalism.

As the industrial revolution proceeded during the nineteenth and into the twentieth century, the economic structure of the Western World became more complex. The classical model no longer fitted. An organizational revolution took place which in many respects fully matched the technological revolution. But the timing and the order of change in the organizational area had special characteristics. Concentration and large-scale organization came first in industry followed by the labor movement and the growth of labor unions. Agricultural organization usually came later. Farmers' group efforts to improve their status are sometimes referred to as the Farmers' Movement. Carl C. Taylor, in his book on this subject, defines a movement as "a type of collective behavior by means of which some large segment of a society attempts to accomplish adjustment of conditions in its economy or culture which it thinks are in maladjustment." [2]

---

1 The discussion of group interests in agriculture presented in this chapter is to be considered illustrative only. Treatment of the history of farmers' organized efforts has filled a number of books and a mere cataloging of all the public and private groups concerned with agriculture with appropriate anatomic description would take many pages and would include numerous names not mentioned here. For general background with respect to what has been christened "countervailing power" one can do no better than refer to the volume by John K. Galbraith, *American Capitalism, The Concept of Countervailing Power,* Houghton Mifflin Co., Boston, 1952. For an even broader setting concerning the growth and status of organized groups in present-day society, see *The Organizational Revolution,* by Kenneth E. Boulding, Harper and Brothers, New York, 1953.

2 Carl C. Taylor, *The Farmers' Movement, 1620–1920,* American Book Co., New York, 1953.

Adam Smith in 1776 believed that competition with a minimum of State interference would correct maladjustments and give each businessman or farmer equality of opportunity. But he did not foresee the economic consequences of the industrial revolution nor realize that business firms in industry would become so large. Although he would have less difficulty than James Watt in picking up the visible threads of the twentieth-century economy, he would probably be even more bewildered and confused if he tried to trace the interlacing web and pattern of economic power. If he were to look at an input-output table showing the interchange of goods and services between industries (table 8-1 is a condensed section from such a table), he would not easily under-

TABLE 8-1.—THE INTERCHANGE OF GOODS AND SERVICES IN THE UNITED STATES BETWEEN AGRICULTURE AND OTHER MAJOR INDUSTRY GROUPS, 1947

Industry groups	Inputs [1]	Outputs [1]
	Billion dollars	*Billion dollars*
Total [2]................................	44.3	44.3
Agriculture and fisheries [3]..................	10.9	10.9
Food, fiber, and selected manufactures........	2.6	18.1
All other manufactures......................	1.7	1.3
Power, transportation, and communication....	1.1	—
Trade......................................	1.4	—
Finance, insurance, and real estate...........	2.6	—
Service industries..........................	0.6	1.2
Inventory change [4]........................	2.7	1.0
Foreign countries [4].......................	0.7	1.3
Government [4].............................	0.8	0.6
Households [4].............................	19.2	9.9

[1] The input column shows the expenditures to various industry groups for resources used in producing agricultural products. The output column shows the distribution of the total agricultural output to various industry groups.

[2] Total output and total input are equal by definition.

[3] This item represents the contribution of the fixed plant. The same value is both an input from agriculture and a distributed part of the output of agriculture (and fisheries).

[4] In the input column are inventory depletions, imports, government payments to farmers, and the value of operator and family labor. In the output column are inventory additions, exports, taxes paid to governments, and farm output consumed in farm households.

Source: Wassily W. Leontief, "Input-Output Economics," *Scientific American*, Oct. 1951, pp. 15–21.

stand how agriculture, for example, could receive so many inputs from other industries and distribute its outputs so far afield. In table 8-1 the first column shows the expense items used by agriculture and the industrial sector from which each is drawn. The second column shows the distribution of the total product of agriculture to each industry group.[3]

Once the meaning of the input-output table was clear, an examination of table 4-1 in Chapter 4, which shows the average number of firms

---

[3] See also Appendix table A-8 for a more complete summary of interchange between the major industry groups.

and the average income per enterprise by major industries, would convince him that the twentieth century is very different from the eighteenth. He would be impressed by the large size and small number of firms in nearly all industries outside of agriculture. He would begin to understand why a labor movement and a farmers' movement have arisen to provide countervailing power for these groups.

In all Western nations the special situation of agriculture led to a recognition of the need for research, education, economic stability, statistics, and regulatory controls. Each nation met these basic needs in its own way. Some countries emphasized cooperative effort; some depended mainly on political organization and legislation; and some used combinations of private, cooperative, and public effort. Whatever the method, it was recognized that certain functions in farm production, marketing, and farm living cannot be carried on efficiently on an individual farm basis, and others cannot be handled at all except through some kind of consolidated or group activity. Individual farms are "the radiant points of competitive energy" that illuminate the scene of action and furnish the initial drive. But we must look to the group interests of agriculture as well to appreciate how the whole of the economic structure is formed and how the economic power generated by the radiant points is brought into focus.

Social changes lag behind technical advances in our civilization. We have only to look around to observe the myriad devices for speeding up and enlarging the material side of life. This side of experience has a big lead. But we must neither overestimate the lead nor doubt too much our ability to bring affairs into better alignment.

Partly because social inventions are usually intangible, we are less sensible of their presence and influence. Consider some of the business institutions that have evolved along with technological change. At one time, individual businessmen or partners controlled most urban business. But, after a long evolution, the present-day limited-liability corporation became the principal vehicle of business management and control. An extended period of hammering on the anvil of public opinion was necessary to bring this mechanism within socially acceptable limits. This process continues.

Certain mechanical innovations were essential before corporations could function efficiently on a large scale. Among the more fundamental were the typewriter, the cash register, the computing machine, and those artificial memory devices—filing systems. Without these synthetic arms and brains, modern business could not have reached its present dimensions. The place of rapid communication and transportation systems is obvious. Equally necessary is the complex banking and credit structure that makes possible the supply of financial lifeblood for the economic bloodstream.

As the corporation evolved in the business world, new services became possible that the small businessman or farmer could not afford to provide for himself. Such services include marketing facilities, carefully controlled research, testing of supplies, advertising, representing the corporation's interest in legislative matters, to mention only a few.

In agriculture most business units are too small to provide enough volume to support any of these activities independently. The need for finding a means of placing farmers on a basis of equal opportunity led early to social invention.

Efforts of the old agricultural societies in the first half of the nineteenth century were directed mainly toward providing farmers with information about better methods of farming. Some cooperative enterprises were developed even in this period as farmers experimented with their mutual problems. Most of these attempts had short careers, but a few persisted and paved the way for the cooperative movement that began around 1870. It should be noted also that legislative sanction for acreage control and price support for tobacco was first sought and obtained in Maryland and Virginia before the middle of the seventeenth century.

Through the years, farmers' efforts to give effect to their group interests have expressed themselves through a succession of farm organizations. Before 1900, several efforts were made to support political parties that appeared to promise hope of resolving the wrongs of the times. The Populist Party was one such vehicle. After 1900, farm organizations became less partisan; they attempted to work for farmers' interests by influencing thinking in both major parties. The National Grange, the oldest of the general farm organizations, has always preferred to endorse positions on issues rather than specific parties or candidates.

Earlier efforts to aid agriculture through legislation took the direction of providing for more education, research, and information on the one hand and for regulation and supervision of railroads and marketing activities on the other.

The embryonic Federal Department of Agriculture first appeared in 1839 when an appropriation of $1,000 was made to the Patent Office to collect crop statistics and distribute seeds. The land-grant college system, to which later were attached the agricultural experiment stations and the agricultural extension services, was inaugurated by the Morrill Act of 1862.

General reform of the banking structure through establishment of the Federal Reserve system in 1914 in the first Wilson administration provided a monetary Gibraltar for many other banking and monetary reforms. Buttressed by this rock, the Federal Farm Loan Act of 1916 permitted erection of the initial structure of farm credit agencies, which is now the Farm Credit Administration.

The 1920's were a depressed period for agriculture, and many plans for aid and relief of farmers were put forth. During this time, legislative assistance and other aid in the formation of farm cooperatives were stressed.

Then came economic collapse and the Great Depression. After the change of administration in 1933, various action programs were instituted to check farm surpluses and bolster up farm prices. Similar measures were attempted for the rest of the total economy.

World War II brought further changes and measures to mobilize limited resources and to direct them effectively toward getting maximum production. The story of the aftermath of the war and the Korean outbreak is still fresh in our minds.

Where are we today? What kind of structure of group interests has agriculture? Recognizing that the form and emphasis that policy and programs take must continually change to fit new circumstances, we can still mark out several broad divisions of group interest. From the viewpoint of the characteristics of the institutions, there are three main categories: (1) farm organizations; (2) farmer cooperatives; (3) government agencies.

This threefold classification is one of convenience; others may prefer a different division. One could start with two categories—governmental and nongovernmental. But the distinction between cooperatives established for specific business purposes and other voluntary farm organizations working in the general area of agricultural interest and policy seems sufficiently fundamental to warrant separate treatment from the outset. One might also consider private business corporations in agricultural lines as an independent group of forces closely related to agriculture. The agricultural press as an instrumentality is not to be overlooked in any analysis of group interests. But some of these aspects must be left for another time.

Farm organizations

In common with all Americans, farmers like to join organizations; they belong to innumerable groups. Many of these are the ones that attract city people, others are mainly concerned with farm interests.

Farm organizations are varied in their makeup, but they may be subdivided into two broad classes—the general-interest and the specific-interest organizations. General-interest organizations try to appeal to all types of farmers regardless of commodity interests. Specific-interest organizations are mainly organized along commodity lines. The distinction is not quite the same as that between craft and industrial unions in labor organizations, but there is a certain parallelism.

The three major general farm organizations of the present day are the American Farm Bureau Federation, the National Grange of the Patrons of Husbandry, and the National Farmers Union. These correspond in agriculture to the great labor unions in organized labor and to certain national associations of businessmen and industrialists in business. Each of the farm organizations has its distinctive characteristics and ideals. Each, as a result of its history, finds its greatest strength in certain parts of the country. Each is national in scope, yet no one of the three, nor even all three combined, represents all farmers.

The American Farm Bureau Federation, with the largest total membership (it reports around 1½ million farm families) has its greatest concentrations of members in the Corn Belt and the Cotton Belt, although its members are well distributed elsewhere too.[4]   The Farm Bureau is a federation of state farm bureaus; it was organized in 1920 by the merging of a number of existing state organizations. It carries on many activities designed to improve returns and living conditions on family farms, and in some states it operates marketing and purchasing cooperatives. It is active in the field of national and state legislation. Because a large proportion of its membership is in the more prosperous commercial farming areas, its influence has been felt most strongly in matters related to commercial farming. The Farm Bureau has been closely associated with the development of the agricultural extension program.

The National Grange has local granges in about three-fourths of the States, but its greatest strength lies in the Northeast and in the Pacific Northwest. Its total membership is about 900,000 persons. The Grange is a fraternal organization; it emphasizes programs for the whole farm family. It sponsors many community activities for farmers, including agricultural fairs, conservation demonstrations, and recreation areas. It is the oldest of the three big farm organizations, having been organized in 1867. The Grange has a long record of support in the field of legislation for freight regulation and in other matters for farmers' benefit, including educational work.

The National Farmers Union is organized in about thirty states and has around a half million individual members.[5]   Its greatest strength is

---

4 The Farm Bureau reports 1,492,282 member families in 1952 in "Forward from Here with Farm Bureau—A Digest of 1953 Policies," American Farm Bureau Federation, December 1952.

5 Comparative data on membership as given in the publication by Jay Judkins, *National Associations of the United States*, U. S. Dept. of Commerce, 1949, are:

American Farm Bureau Federation	1,250,000
National Grange	800,000
National Farmers Union	450,000

The *1954 World Almanac* records:

American Farm Bureau Federation	1,492,282
National Grange	900,000
National Farmers Union	Not given

Note that the Farm Bureau counts memberships by family heads and the National Grange and Farmers Union counts memberships by individual members of the family of certain ages and status.

in the wheat-producing states of the northern Great Plains and in Arkansas, Kansas, and Oklahoma.   The Farmers Union like the Farm Bureau and the Grange stresses the significance of the family farm, and it supports measures to help small farmers.   It sponsors educational programs and operates a number of cooperative businesses.   The legislative program of the Farmers Union at state and national levels reflects the background of the areas in which many of its members live.   The Great Plains is a region of high risk and uncertainty with extremes of weather and yields; its farmers have frequently been in financial straits. This partly explains the relatively greater stress of the Farmers Union on programs of financial security.

These three major general farm organizations have much in common. They frequently take the same position on national agricultural issues. Their differences arise mainly from the different economic backgrounds of their major constituents.   Specific-interest farm organizations, which usually have a commodity focus, also take positions on general questions.   These organizations include some of the cooperative groups mentioned below.   Still other farm-oriented organizations such as the National Cotton Council of America may also act in the farmer's field of interest.

But many farmers belong to no farm organization.   The three major national farm organizations taken together probably include only a little more than a third of all farm operators and perhaps half of the commercial farmers.   Low-income and noncommercial farmers are especially underrepresented in the membership of these organizations.

Farmer cooperatives

More than 60,000 separate farmer cooperatives were listed in 1954 by the Farmer Cooperative Service on the basis of reports from such associations.   No one overhead group represents all these cooperatives on a national basis.   But the National Council for Farmer Cooperatives, organized in 1929, provides general educational and promotional services for many of them.   The Council assists member cooperatives in deciding upon general policies, in legislative matters, in keeping farmers informed of current developments that affect cooperation, and in other matters of mutual interest.   In many respects the Council can also be regarded as a general farm organization, because it concerns itself with national agricultural problems in the broadest sense.

The Cooperative League of USA is a national organization that includes a fairly large number of farm purchasing cooperatives, which have joined with urban cooperative purchasing associations in a common educational program.

A number of other national organizations represent the special interests of particular cooperative commodity or service groups.   Examples are the National Livestock Producers' Association, the National Milk Producers' Federation, the National Federation of Grain Cooperatives, and the National Rural Electric Cooperative Association.

It is estimated that farmers' cooperative associations handle about a fifth of all farm products sold and about a fifth of the farm supplies purchased. On the farm supply side, feeds, fertilizer, and farm equipment are big items. The significance of the farmer cooperative movement in marketing, purchasing, and servicing is greater than one might think from the percentages of the total volume of goods handled. Cooperatives frequently have promoted new and more efficient methods, introduced fresh competition, increased returns to farmers, lifted prevailing standards of business practice, and served as pilot operations for larger segments of an industry. Probably three in five farmers in the country belong to one or more cooperative organizations.[6]

From time to time the cooperative movement has enlisted much good will and energy and some measure of the crusading spirit that is necessary to put new ventures into effect. Cooperation holds a high place on the margin of the new economic frontier. Recent examples of service cooperatives include those organized for telephones, electricity, medical care, livestock breeding, and seed improvement.

Although we may think first of cooperative marketing and purchasing associations, cooperatives have been successful in other fields. For example, approximate numbers of farmer cooperatives by types as listed in 1953 are given in the accompanying tabulation.[7]

Production	13,380
Marketing and purchasing	9,977
Financing	2,206
Mutual fire insurance	1,800
Telephone and electric	33,811
Rural health	51
Total	61,225

Production cooperatives listed include mutual irrigation companies, dairy herd improvement associations, artificial breeding associations, and grazing associations.

In essence, the cooperative is a type of corporation that is especially suited to performing certain jobs in connection with agriculture. An ordinary corporation is designed to make profits for its stockholders by performing services for others. A cooperative corporation is designed

---

6 As of June 30, 1953, Rural Electrification Administration reported 3,753,000 members of cooperative electric power and light associations. It is estimated that about 70 percent of these were farmers, which would make approximately 2,627,000 farmer members. In other words, nearly half of all farmers were members of electric cooperatives. As areas served by other electric companies also contain many other types of cooperatives, the percentage of all farmers who are members of at least one cooperative must be considerably higher.

7 U. S. Dept. of Agriculture, *Agricultural Statistics*, 1953, p. 591.

to lower the costs of performing services for its members. The fundamental characteristic of a cooperative is that it is operated for the
mutual benefit of its members as producers (or consumers)—not as
stockholders. Benefits to a member come primarily through patronage
of the association and not in the form of returns for any financial investment that may have been made. A cooperative enables farmers to
make use of the corporate form of business organization for performing
certain production and marketing functions that cannot be performed
efficiently by individual farm operators. At the same time a cooperative permits farmers to maintain their basic competitive independence.

A farm cooperative is thus a modified form of a corporation adjusted
to fit agricultural conditions. Farmer members usually have more voice
in the affairs of the cooperative than do stockholders in an ordinary
business corporation, although at times this "voice" may become at-
tenuated and management of the cooperative may become institutional-
ized.

Government

The brief historical sketch of government services for agriculture
given earlier suggests how some of these services have evolved to fit a
changing outlook. Many of these developments, especially those of recent years, have been on a national basis, but one should not lose sight
of the important role played by state governments. Many services, too,
are on a joint federal-state basis. The land-grant college system, the
federal-state crop-and-livestock estimating system, public roads, and
many regulatory activities (grades and standards, for example) are
operated in this way.

The role of government in the affairs of agriculture has expanded in
the last 50 years, in response to a widely felt need to balance the
economic advantages and power brought into being by corporations and
big business and later by labor unions on the part of urban employees
in mass employment industries. This is not to say that business and
labor have not sought and gained significant government aid, too. One
has only to mention the tariff and minimum-wage legislation to remember ways in which the strong arm of the Nation furnishes support to
occupational groups other than agriculture.

But the ways of attaining economic advantage in business and labor
did not work equally well in agriculture. Farm organizations and
farm cooperatives went part way. Invention of further instruments
with the aid of government seemed the way out.[8] So the agricultural

---

8 Sometimes social inventions of this general origin take the form of government agencies, sometimes that of new private or cooperative institutions initially sponsored and aided by legislation,
and not infrequently combinations of the two approaches.

forces turned to state and federal legislation to set up a series of special institutions designed to provide comparable economic advantage and power for farmers.[9] The functions performed by these institutions have to do with growth and development in these fields: [10]

1. Education.
2. New technology.
3. Economics of production and marketing.
4. Rules of the game.
5. Information on economic conditions.
6. Credit facilities.
7. Price and adjustment programs.
8. Conservation.

Education. Farm people have shared with urban people in the general improvement in publicly supported education that has taken place at all stages from primary schools through colleges and universities. The sharing has sometimes come more slowly in rural areas. But in a sense the firm establishment of the principle of public education has benefited farm people more than other groups in the population. Any alternative system would almost certainly have meant a relatively greater lack of opportunity for farm children. Experience in other parts of the world demonstrates this plainly.

Above the secondary level, the most significant landmark in the history of education for farm people was the federal legislation for establishment of land-grant colleges for "agriculture and the mechanic arts" by the Morrill Act of 1862. A few states had started agricultural colleges earlier, but this legislation really founded the system.

Land-grant colleges represented a break with the formal tradition that looked on colleges as training grounds for a select few in a limited number of professional fields. These were to be "poor men's colleges" for the practical training of young people in the ordinary vocations of life. Here was the first great experiment in mass education at the highest level. Out of this context, the social dignity of work in agriculture, home economics, and engineering has been raised to the same level as in other professional fields. By thus lifting and broadening the base of professional training, the Nation has not only benefited from the more productive application of human effort, but many false social distinctions have been avoided.

Improvement in general education has meant that farm people learn

---

9 Whether farm organizations or major political parties have been the more significant agencies in initiating new legislation is a debated question. Scrutiny of the history of the political campaigns of 1948 and 1952 as well as earlier ones suggests that both were deeply involved.

10 This listing of fields is far from complete, but it is intended to be suggestive. Probably most government activities related to agriculture could be fitted under these headings, but a complete classification might be quite different. Where does rural free delivery of mail belong, for example? Where would one place weather forecasting?

about new technical methods more readily and participate more intelligently in decisions concerning economic and social matters. With greater understanding of the probable consequences of alternative actions, they can be better citizens and can better safeguard their own group economic interests.

The Cooperative Federal-State Extension Service also represents a field of educational effort in which agriculture has broken with tradition. State colleges of agriculture and the United States Department of Agriculture, working with voluntary groups, carried on some informal educational work even before the present pattern of extension work was established by the passage of the Federal Extension Act in 1914. Most of the 3,000 counties in the United States now have at least one county agricultural agent and one home demonstration agent who works with farm women. Extension work with farm youth is also carried on through 4-H Clubs and otherwise. County workers are backed up by state subject-matter specialists who are members of corresponding departments in the state colleges and who keep in touch with latest developments in research and demonstration results.

New technology. Large corporations have their own research laboratories and they can afford to carry on extensive research. But few farmers would find the time and energy, to say nothing of the money, necessary to carry on controlled experiments. Hence, agricultural experiment stations were established at government expense to carry on such work. The research facilities of the land-grant colleges and the United States Department of Agriculture form a single system, with the various federal laboratories closely interlocked with the experiment stations of the colleges and universities and with the agricultural extension service. This is the joint federal-state system. Out of it has come a major part of the technical knowledge and the educational drive that has made possible the expansion in farm production that has taken place since the approximate geographic boundaries of our land resources were reached.

Throughout the greater part of the history of the United States the frontier was a *land* frontier. The influence of the westward-marching boundary was very great on many phases of the Nation's growth. New farms and ranches were carved out of forests, prairies, plains, and mountain valleys. Farm output more than kept pace with expanding population, and surpluses were shipped abroad as well. By 1920, nearly all the land suitable for agriculture had been taken up and the land frontier was no more.

Technology has always been a factor. But, at about the same time that the outer rim of the land frontier was reached, the full impact of new methods began to show up in farm output. Technology represents the new frontier that lies before us, and its boundaries stretch into the unknown. Most historians have pointed out that the outstanding circumstance in our agricultural history has been the continuous long-time presence of the land frontier. Fewer perhaps have recognized the new technological frontier and its significance to agriculture.

Differences in the social responsibilities involved in the two frontiers are worth more than a passing remark. The land frontier was the Nation's safety valve, and, except for a few significant institutional devices for ensuring a minimum of control over land entry and development, the process of occupation was an individualistic one. Men were free to develop the farm resources as they came to them.

The new technological frontier is different. The land frontier was in a sense a natural frontier; the technological frontier is man made, mainly by conscious group effort. What we have done is to provide a social mechanism (laboratories, experiment stations, etc.) largely at public expense.

Private industry, too, conducts significant *agricultural* research. Industrial expenditures for such research now total more than those of the United States Department of Agriculture and state agricultural experiment stations together. Estimates by the Agricultural Research Service based on information from several government agencies and the National Research Council indicate that recent annual expenditures by industry for research on agricultural products and on machinery and materials used in agriculture were in excess of $140 million. This compares with expenditures by United States Department of Agriculture and the state agricultural experiment stations in the fiscal year 1953 of $118 million. Expenditures for agricultural research on the part of other public institutions (mainly endowed colleges and state universities not in the land-grant college system) are not included in this total. How much these institutions spent is not known, but for forestry research alone their expenditures were nearly half as much as the total spent for forestry research by the United States Department of Agriculture and the state agricultural experiment stations.

About four-fifths of the total agricultural research money of the United States Department of Agriculture and the state agricultural experiment stations is used for research on subjects that directly aid farm production, as compared with only about a third of that used by industry. The industry third is used mainly for research on farm machinery and agricultural chemicals. The greater part of the other two-thirds of the industrial research related to agriculture has to do with the utilization and marketing of farm products. Although the total sums spent by government and industry on *agricultural* research are not far apart, the money spent on developing new technology in farm production comes largely from public sources.

The total research mechanism supplies a stream of new technology which flows freely into use on existing farms. In the absence of effective social control on inputs or outputs, this means that farm output at times tends to rise and to surge against a less rapidly expanding demand.[11] The fact that the demand for most farm products is relatively inelastic (a given percentage change in supply results in a much greater percentage change in price) also means that excessive production is likely to have disastrous effects on prices and income.

Uncertainty exists as to the nature of the flow of new technology, both with respect to the rate at which innovations come over the horizon and the length of time it takes to obtain their widespread adoption.[12]

Cochrane and Lampe believe that the reserve of technology now on the horizon and likely to be coming over is large enough to assure a continuous flow of applied innnovations that will exert an upward pressure on supplies of farm products. Trelogan and Johnson are more impressed by the episodic or erratic nature of the flow of technology and the need for continued emphasis on research to provide the basis for increased levels of production necessary for our increasing population.

Most observers agree that sharp fluctuations in demand may push the economy into episodic periods of surplus or deficit, simply because corresponding short-run adjustments in farm output are difficult.

One must keep in mind this general background of social encouragement of research, as well as the organization of agriculture and its biological characteristics, to understand why farmers seek public assistance in controlling output and in adjusting farm operations during such a transition period as the 1950's.

Some may infer from this that a simple solution to the farm-surplus problem would be to shut down all laboratory and experiment station activities until demand caught up with supplies. If we were willing to live in a static economy, this might eventually solve part of the problem. But other things are wrong with the inference. First, any cessation of agricultural research activity would not be reflected in lowered rates of adoption of new technology for several years because of the reservoir of research findings always on hand. Second, for corresponding reasons, if shortages were to arise in the absence of continuing research, it would take years to redevelop experiment stations, to obtain

---

11 This also occurred from time to time on the land frontier, but the difference between the two frontiers is something like that between a bolt of lightning from the skies and a similar bolt of electricity from a short circuit in a high-power line. The one arises from Nature, and damage from it is thought of as an act of Providence; but harm from the other is attributed to the shortcomings of man.

12 See the presentation of opposing views in the following: Willard W. Cochrane and Harlan C. Lampe, "The Nature of the Race Between Food Supplies and Demand in the U. S., 1951–1975," *Journal of Farm Economics*, May 1953; Harry C. Trelogan and Neil W. Johnson, "The Evitability of Technological Advance," *Journal of Farm Economics*, Nov. 1953; and also the Cochrane-Lampe "Rejoinder" in the same Nov. 1953 *Journal*.

research results, and to work out their applications. Research is the kind of productive activity that must be kept alive and growing if it is to be successful. Timing a research organization and shutting it off and on would be many times more difficult than outguessing the business cycle. The crucial point is that a society that supports research in agriculture to the extent that this nation has done, has an implied obligation to help farmers and others make some of the subsequent adjustments that flow from the impact of research results.

Economics of production and marketing. With the rise of technical knowledge and its application in farming came a growing awareness of economic problems. But attempts to deal with the economic phases of agriculture got under way slowly. A few beginnings were made before 1900, but it was not until 1902 that the Secretary of Agriculture approved the establishment of the Office of Farm Management in the Bureau of Plant Industry. By 1915, this office had achieved independent status and reported directly to the Secretary. The early focus in farm management work in the Department of Agriculture and in the state colleges was on economic problems of individual farms. Many agricultural surveys and cost studies were made. After the Bureau of Agricultural Economics was established in the Department under the first Secretary Wallace, in 1922, the viewpoint broadened to take cognizance of regional and national economic problems of agriculture. To many, the key seemed primarily a question of marketing, and in government assistance to farmers and to farm cooperatives, marketing has been stressed again and again through the years. In the Cooperative Marketing Act of 1926, for example, a program directed toward the cooperative marketing and purchasing problems of farmers was emphasized. The program of research and service to cooperatives then initiated is continued by the Farmer Cooperative Service of the United States Department of Agriculture.[13]

We are so accustomed to accepting public highways as a part of the natural order of things that we may not think of these means of transportation in terms of their contributions to farm marketing and to elimination of rural isolation. The part played by the Bureau of Public Roads at the national level and by various state agencies in administering federal and state highway construction is written large on the record of the twentieth century. Automobiles and all-weather highways are the twin gifts of private and public enterprise.

The United States Department of Agriculture has conducted research in the problems of marketing for many years. The Agricultural Marketing Act of 1946 (RMA, Title II) following World War II made

---

13 The 1953 reorganization of the Department of Agriculture placed its functions in four main groups, and these groups were divided into *Services*. The *Service* designation thus became the major agency title, replacing the older term *Bureau*.

available additional support for marketing research both in the Department and in the land-grant colleges.

In appraising the effect of marketing research on output, it is difficult to reach definitive conclusions. In many respects, developments in marketing are parallel to those in production. We have been more successful in growing two blades of grass where one grew before and in providing more marketing services than in balancing output and consumption. In this area, many problems still confront us.

Rules of the game. Under any system of economic enterprise, some broad rules and some umpires or referees are needed to keep the game going properly. The public interest is usually best served by an umpire or regulating agency that is responsible to government.

The Interstate Commerce Commission, the Food and Drug Administration, and the Commodity Exchange Authority are among such regulatory agencies in the federal government. The Agricultural Research and Agricultural Marketing Services in the United States Department of Agriculture carry on many regulatory programs related to control and eradication of plant and animal diseases and to standardization, testing, and inspection of farm products. The state departments of agriculture usually have authority to enforce grades and standards, to supervise sanitary measures, to test feeds and fertilizers, and the like. To set up fair standards and to make sure that trade is kept honest and fair to all concerned is a necessary job. Much of this work is done so efficiently that the general public is almost unaware of its significance. Occasionally some lapse or breakdown brings a controversy into the open and shows the need for further reform in the legislative or administrative field.

Economic values affected by regulatory supervision in agriculture are far greater than is usually appreciated. For example, the dollar value of futures trading in regulated farm commodities in the fiscal year 1952–1953 was more than $2\frac{1}{2}$ times that of the trading in stocks and bonds on the 16 registered security exchanges.[14] In round numbers the values were nearly $46 billion and $18 billion, respectively. The regulation of futures trading and speculation in commodity markets is essential for maintaining fair and open competitive dealings. Futures prices affect cash prices, not only in the large terminal markets but in the local markets and country points where farmers sell their products.

Information on economic conditions. Equal access to knowledge about market supplies and prices is essential to a freely operating market. Here the services provided by state and federal crop-and-livestock estimates and statistics on prices paid and prices received by farmers and current market-news reports are among the basic types

---

14 U. S. Dept. of Agriculture, *Report of the Administrator of the Commodity Exchange Authority,* 1953, p. 2.

of information. Without this information from some reliable source, commodity markets could scarcely function. Only a public agency can ensure the availability of such information on an equally impartial basis for all.

Beyond provision for the collection and dissemination of current information on farm production, marketings, and prices, are such matters as construction and maintenance of index numbers of current economic change, analysis of the economic situation for farm commodities individually and collectively, and analysis and interpretation of the longer-term economic situation and outlook. In each of these fields public agencies have taken a leading part.

Credit facilities. "Capital rationing" is a phrase that has come into use in recent years to indicate an undue restriction of credit on those who are in position to use it effectively. Because banking and credit institutions were first designed with urban business in mind, they did not meet farmers' needs. For a long time farmers were disadvantaged with respect to short- and especially long-term loans because institutional machinery was not available to serve them.

One of the important effects of the establishment of government-sponsored credit agencies has been their influence on the lending practices of private credit agencies. Many private agencies now make long-term amortized farm loans, approve carefully budgeted lines of credit for an entire production period, and advance funds only as needed and charge interest only for the time funds are actually used. Like cooperatives, public credit agencies have acted as trail-breakers and pace-setters in introducing and carrying forward improved practices. As indicated earlier, private agencies provide a large volume of agricultural credit and most of this is on terms suited to the needs of the industry.

The Farm Credit Administration, the Farmers Home Administration, and the Rural Electrification Administration have been developed to fill particular categories of need that were not at one time adequately supplied by private banking interests.

The Farm Credit Administration in its several constituent agencies is a source of credit for long-term land purchases, and for short-term production uses. The arm known as the Bank for Cooperatives supplies credit for cooperative organizations.

Local farm loan and production credit associations set up under the sponsorship of the Farm Credit Administration are farmer cooperatives with original capital advanced from public funds. Provision was made in the law for gradual repayment of this capital. The farm loan associations have done this, and they are now entirely self-sufficient cooperatives, relying only on federal supervision and guarantees. This whole operation over the years represents a unique partnership of public and private funds, with gradual withdrawal of public funds as the organization gains maturity.

The Farmers Home Administration provides a form of supervised credit for less-well-established farmers, which includes a complete farm-and-home plan as a preliminary condition of the loan and close supervision and assistance in seeing that the plan is carried out. This specialized type of service was developed to reduce the risk and uncertainty that would otherwise militate against the making of such loans.

The Rural Electrification Administration furnishes a special form of credit to rural electric and telephone companies and cooperatives that meet certain specified conditions, particularly with respect to area coverage and technical facilities. The technical assistance furnished is a significant element in the success that this agency has had in promoting electrification for farms. Nearly 80 percent of the farms of the country were electrified by 1950 as compared with about 10 percent in 1930. This result appears to be due mainly to a combination of cooperative effort on the part of farmers and of private enterprise in the field of electrical supplies and equipment in a period of favorable incomes.

Price and adjustment programs. The kinds of institutional assistance described above are now accepted by most friends of agriculture as essential jobs that can best be performed with public participation. In view of the way the rest of the economy operates, it is necessary to make such services available, usually with the assistance of government. Differences in view arise almost entirely over minor elements of form and content. Production adjustment, price support, surplus disposal, conservation, and related measures bring out more cleavages in opinion. They are areas in which the ebb and flow of opinion and pressure are certain to continue. Hence, any precise description of structure is likely to be soon outdated.

In two extreme types of emergency situations, general agreement has been reached. In the event of major war, it is a foregone conclusion that important production and price intervention in agriculture, as in other parts of the economy, will be prompt and far reaching. And in the event of catastrophic depression or drought little time will be lost in giving aid. But in less extreme situations there lies a middle ground of unsettled problems.

The war and postwar years, with their continuing high demand for farm products, have put off the most embarrassing questions. But the pressure points are still there. Existing legislation provides for a number of adjustment and price-supporting operations to be brought into play under certain conditions. In general, there are perhaps two broad groupings of programs.

Under the first heading are the market agreement and order programs for perishables. These programs differ from commodity to commodity.

They use a variety of devices, including diversion of supplies into non-commercial as well as lower-order uses.

Under the second heading are price-support and crop-loan programs. The issues here turn around the level of price support to aim at, whether supports should be flexible or rigid, and whether efforts should be made to redirect production into other channels.

Marketing agreements and orders. Marketing agreement and order programs are used mainly for perishables and are carried on under authority of the Agricultural Marketing Act of 1937, as amended. These programs provide a method of bargaining for producers and seek to establish and maintain orderly marketing conditions for certain commodities and their products. In 1953, marketing agreement and order programs were in effect for milk, fruit, vegetables, tree nuts, and hops.

Milk order programs provide for classification of milk on the basis of use and for establishment of minimum prices that must be paid producers for the milk that goes into each use. An order applies to a designated milkshed or marketing area, as for example, the New York marketing area.

On other commodities, marketing agreements and orders control grade, size, and quantities that may be marketed from production areas as, for example, the Florida citrus-growing area.

In all instances, these orders are established at the request of producers. They must be approved by a two-thirds majority of the producers voting in a referendum. They can be voted out at any time by a majority of producers affected by the order either by number or volume. They may be suspended by the Secretary of Agriculture if he determines that they fail to achieve the declared policy of the Agricultural Marketing Act of 1937, as amended.

Price supports and crop loans. Price-support and crop-loan programs are administered by the United States Department of Agriculture through the Commodity Credit Corporation and the Commodity Stabilization Service.

Under the price-support program, price minimums, or floors, are established for many commodities. Support at these levels is achieved through loans, purchases, agreements to purchase, or sometimes through a combination of these methods. Price support for corn, cotton, wheat, rice, tobacco, and peanuts—so-called basic commodities—is mandatory. Support is also mandatory for certain designated nonbasic commodities —wool, mohair, tung nuts, honey, milk, and butterfat. For most other commodities, support is permissive at the direction of the Secretary of Agriculture.[15]

---

[15] Statements here and elsewhere state the situation as of the beginning of 1954, before congressional action had been taken on any proposals then pending. For details see *U. S. Dept. Agr. Inf. Bul. 13,* "Price Programs of the United States Department of Agriculture," revised, Dec. 1953.

The level of support varies by commodities, but, in general, it is based upon the prevailing parity level. Parity may be defined roughly as the level of farm prices that will give farm commodities the same buying power they had in the base period 1910–1914, when prices received and paid were considered to be in good balance. For example if 2 bushels of wheat bought a pair of overalls in the base period, they should do the same today. For "basic" commodities (corn, wheat, tobacco, rice, and peanuts), the support level, as determined by legislation, must be at 90 percent of parity through the crop year 1954.

For the designated nonbasic commodities (wool, mohair, honey, tung nuts, milk, and butterfat), the support level is not more than 90 percent of parity, not less than 60 percent for the first four commodities, and not less than 75 percent for milk and butterfat as determined by the Secretary of Agriculture under certain conditions. The level of support for other commodities is not mandatory; it is permissive at any level not in excess of 90 percent after consideration of various factors by the Secretary. These factors include availability of funds and willingness of producers to make production adjustments.

Crop loans are made on commodities in approved storage by local credit institutions. County committees, as agents for the Commodity Credit Corporation, inspect the stored commodity and the storage facilities, and, if they are acceptable, guarantee the loan to the lender. These are called "nonrecourse" loans. They are made without recourse to the borrower, that is, the Commodity Credit Corporation is willing to accept the commodity as settlement of the obligation, and producers are not required to make good any loss incurred through a decline in the market price.

For farmers who cannot meet storage requirements or who do not desire to retain title to the commodity, the Commodity Credit Corporation offers price supports in the form of "agreements to purchase" at stated prices, which are at comparable levels to the loan value.

The Commodity Credit Corporation makes direct purchases as a part of surplus-removal operations, presumably of perishable commodities. Subsidy payments are made to exporters to sell certain surplus commodities in the world market. Some differential payments are also made at times to enable processors to buy surplus commodities at support prices and divert them to by-product or new uses.

Production adjustments. A fundamental dilemma presents itself when price supports are used as backstops to maintain farm prices and income. Prices perform a dual role. They serve to distribute income from past production, and they act as income indicators and incentives for future production. Price supports that treat farmers with equity in the first role are likely to make a bad job of the second. Resources do not readily move in the direction of more desirable alternatives if producers expect favorable future prices for the commodities they currently produce.

Production quota and acreage allotment programs are one method of dealing with this dilemma. These programs permit maintenance of prices at some percentage of parity and force reduction of acreage by allotting each grower a lower acreage of a particular crop, which cannot be exceeded without penalty. These programs have had some success in holding production in check temporarily, but experience has also shown that growers intensify their operations. They use the better land, apply more fertilizer, and follow improved practices, so that output per acre is considerably increased.

The flexible price plan would let price supports rise or fall within limits according to a graduated plan, depending on the size of surplus stocks. Although this plan has been part of the agricultural law for several years, its application was postponed by Congress. Critics point out that flexible prices have a political weakness. This is the appearance of progressive departure from parity support levels and the fact that their chief application would come in periods when strongest pressures for income support would probably arise. If a way can be devised to couple the flexible price plan with some method of income support during the transition period to a different pattern of production, the plan may become more acceptable.

Section-32 programs for widening markets. The farm-surplus problem may also be dealt with by widening market outlets for farm products. In 1935 Congress passed legislation especially aimed at this front. This is commonly referred to as Section 32 (Section 32 of Public Law Number 320, Seventy-Fourth Congress). With later legislation, it authorizes encouragement of exports of farm commodities and encouragement of domestic consumption of farm commodities by diversion from normal trade channels, by increasing utilization by low-income groups, and by other methods, including school lunch programs. Section 32 provides for a continuing appropriation in an amount equal to 30 percent of the gross receipts collected under the custom laws, for carrying out these programs.

Total expenditures under Section 32 by type of program for the fiscal years 1936–1953 are given in the accompanying tabulation.

	Million dollars
Domestic direct distribution programs....	669
Food stamp plan (1939–1943)...........	262
Export programs......................	272
Diversion programs...................	106
Cotton stamp plan (1940–1942).........	24
Total for commodities................	1,333
School lunch cash payments............	137
Administrative expenses...............	60
Total expenditures...................	1,530

Conservation. Conservation has had a deep and fundamental appeal to Americans since the followers of Theodore Roosevelt and Gifford Pinchot focused a widespread half-conscious feeling that something needed to be done if future generations were to share in the natural resources of this continent.

In the structure of current government programs for conservation of soil and water and development of land, major items include: (1) The agricultural conservation and development programs of the Agricultural Conservation Program Service, the Soil Conservation Service and associated local Soil Conservation districts, and the Forest Service, in the Department of Agriculture; related programs of the Bureau of Reclamation and the Bureau of Land Management in the Department of the Interior and (2) the flood-control programs of the Forest and Soil Conservation Services in the Department of Agriculture; and those of the Corps of Engineers, U. S. Army; the Bureau of Reclamation, Department of the Interior; some state, city, and local governments; and the Tennessee Valley Authority.

Basically the goal of public conservation must rest on achievement of a measure of conservation (and development) that would be desirable in the long-run national interest and that would not be achieved by private individuals without some public assistance. Public investment in conservation must be justified on the basis of public welfare. Although it is mixed with many other objectives, this is a common ideal of each public agency that has to do with conservation.

The Soil Conservation Service, for example, furnishes technical advice and assistance in making conservation plans for farms and in carrying out long-range conservation programs. The agricultural conservation payments program, administered by the Agricultural Conservation Program Service, is designed to assist farmers to follow conservation practices that they might otherwise adopt more slowly or not at all.

The Forest Service and the Bureau of Land Management touch agricultural operators most directly through watershed protection and control of grazing on public lands under their jurisdictions. Improper lumbering and excessive rates of stocking are destructive and can cause permanent damage. Administration of forest lands obviously has many other indirect relationships to commercial farming. In addition to regulating grazing and timber cutting on federal lands, these agencies look after fire control, revegetation of erodible land, and similar matters. Forest Service personnel in forest areas advise farmers on problems of forest and range management that are related to conservation on privately owned lands.

CHAPTER 9

SOCIAL FEATURES OF THE STRUCTURE
OF AGRICULTURE

So far in this book the business side of farming has been emphasized. This chapter is intended to focus more light on farm people and the social structure of agriculture. What are some of the main features of the living of farm people? How does the content of their living, broadly considered, compare with that of urban people? Usually we contrast the differences between city and country and neglect the similarities. But the more significant single conclusion might now be in terms of the growing similarity between urban and rural social conditions. As the processes of "urbanization" of rural areas go still further, the differences are likely to be even fewer. But certain differences will remain if only because of the combination of social and economic life that prevails in farming.

A family on a farm is a basic social and economic unit in a more striking sense than is a family in a city. Farming has often been termed "a way of life," and this expression underscores the thought that more than the business of making money is involved.

Family farming has been variously defined. One brief definition is this:

> A family farm or ranch is one which provides the main source of income for the farm family, on which the farm operator (owner or tenant) or members of his family make most of the managerial decisions, participate regularly in farm work, and normally supply a substantial part of the labor needed to operate the farm.[1]

This definition is broad enough to include nearly all family farm units in the United States, except part-time, residential and sharecropper units, and even they have many characteristics of family operation.

The family farm concept is a real and vital one. But, in much of the contemporary discussion of farming, the term "family farm" wears a special halo. This marked luminosity has been vividly presented by many writers. The following example puts it very well:

---

[1] U. S. Dept. of Agriculture, "The Family Farm's Future," *PA 168*, June 1951, p. 3.

It is no concession to mythology to recognize the popularity of the family farm as a symbol of the good life in the United States. Plato says the ideal forms of human institutions are laid away in heaven; but this one is not. It is the daydream of city-dwellers, the inspiration of poets and artists, the biographer's security for the youth of great men. It stands for democracy in its purest and most classic form. For millions of Americans, it represents a better world, past but not quite lost, one to which they may still look for individual happiness or, maybe, national salvation.[2]

One needs to recognize that this "halo effect" surrounds all our thinking about the farm and the farm home. The historical significance and connection with the evolution of our general institutions is evident. The long succession of public measures having to do with land ownership from colonial times to the present are links in a chain that connects many democratic institutions in our social structure. Land was the chief form of wealth in former ages, and the leaders in the new world were so close to the feudal restrictions of the old world that they wished to keep land widely distributed as an aid to political and social democracy. In this they were successful.

But the record of the past should not cloud current judgment. The family farm will stand or fall on its merits in today's scheme of things. The *Deserted Village* of Goldsmith and the fate of the English yeoman class were tragedies that fire the imagination, but they have little bearing on the present.

Today the family farm is very much a going concern, but its relative place in the national scene is greatly reduced by the growth of the urban economy. Other institutions in the social structure will henceforward carry greater weight. The family farm will continue to make its contribution to the social fabric, but it will be as a part of a greater whole. In this great synthesis, part-time and residential farming and country living will play an integrating role.

Involvement of the family in agriculture. The definition of the family farm given above sets out the essential interrelationships between the farm family and the farm business. The farm operator furnishes most of the management, he and his family supply most of the labor, and he owns part or all of the capital invested in the business. Some of the other differences between farm and city ways of life disappeared as barriers of distance and communication were eliminated. The isolation that formerly affected farm life is of less consequence. The farm family is now exposed to nearly the same pressures that impinge upon the city family, and social interactions take place in a much wider sphere.[3]

2 A. Whitney Griswold, *Farming and Democracy*, Yale University Press, New Haven, 1952, p. 5.

3 A daily notebook kept by the author's great grandfather on a farm in northern Illinois in the 1850's discloses a pattern of neighborhood interaction between families and in relation to outside influences that makes a fascinating contrast with the present. The sharing of equipment, labor, and

French Canadians take pride in the ancient customs and ways that have been preserved on the remote farms and villages of Quebec. Large, closely knit families continue to live and work much as they did a century or more ago. Other small groups have tried here and there to maintain the old ways as long as possible. But they are the exceptions. Usually strong religious sanctions and able leadership are essential elements in maintaining such groups in active being. The fact that most such movements have relied on an agricultural setting for their economic base, shows how close the tie-up can be between the family and agriculture. The regularly recurring round of the seasons, the biological phenomena of farm life, recall ancient memories from distant times when life depended on the success of farming.

The old days are gone, but the relationship between the farm and the family remains unique in many ways. The economy of the farm is close at hand, visible to every member of the family and participated in by everyone. This is rarely so in other occupations in which the head of the family works far from home at a job that his family may know little about. A family whose members live and work together is certain to be a more closely knit unit than one that has its activities scattered over a wider range.

Apparently both the rural and the urban family in this country are evolving toward what social scientists call the small, isolated, middle-class family of the conjugal type. This means a family consisting of a father and mother and children until they reach adult life. Wider kinship groupings characteristic of former times have given way before the growing variety of economic opportunities and the substitution of occupational status for older ways of acquiring social position. The strains and stresses that influence family life are reflected in the statistics of broken families, in emotional disorders, and in the greater instability of modern social life. No doubt these ills will be corrected in time as people gradually learn to live more orderly lives in the new world that has been unlocked by science and technology. Farm families may have a considerable advantage in working out desirable adjustments because they are not subjected to so much centrifugal force in the daily whirl of events. The closer welding together of farm and home activities helps to offset the outward pull of events.

Income and supplemental employment

Income is a useful compass for many guiding purposes; we turn to it to take our bearings with respect to how farm families compare with all families in the United States. Most income analyses of farm census information are limited to gross income data. A special study of data

---

even money was on an informal basis not to be thought of now. Neighborhood and kinship ties were closer and more intense; distant ties were weaker and in some cases absent altogether.

from the 1950 Census of Population and the 1950 Census of Agriculture in which census schedules from each source were "matched together" furnished for the first time detailed net money income data for farm-operator families by economic classes of farms.[4]

Many technical difficulties arise in dealing with income data, and especially farm income data. These are touched upon lightly in this discussion, because of lack of time and space. In table 9-1 are the

TABLE **9-1.**—DISTRIBUTION OF FARM-OPERATOR FAMILIES AND ALL FAMILIES BY TOTAL MONEY INCOME, UNITED STATES, 1949

Item	Farm-operator families	All families
	Thousands	*Thousands*
Total number of families....	5,380	38,311
Number reporting income....	4,856	36,440
	Percentage distribution by total family income	
	Percent	*Percent*
Total farms reporting...	100.0	100.0
Income group: [1]		
Under $1,000............	28.1	14.7
$1,000 to 1,999..........	24.8	14.6
$2,000 to 2,999..........	17.8	19.1
$3,000 to 3,999..........	11.8	19.4
$4,000 to 4,999..........	6.8	12.1
$5,000 to 5,999..........	3.5	7.8
$6,000 to 6,999..........	2.2	4.3
$7,000 to 9,999..........	2.8	4.9
$10,000 and over........	2.2	3.1

NOTE.—Total money income is a net cash income concept. For farm-operator families it includes value of farm products sold minus expenses; net returns from nonfarm business and professional practice carried on by operators or members of their families; and wages, salaries, and other income received by operators and members of their families.

[1] Median money income for farm-operator families was $1,867, and for all families $3,073. Medians computed from $500 income intervals.

Source: U. S. Dept. of Commerce and U. S. Dept. of Agriculture, *Farms and Farm People, A Special Cooperative Report*, June 1953, p. 25.

comparative distributions of total money income of farm-operator families and of all families in the United States. The distribution for farm-operator families is much more heavily weighted in the lower income groups than that for all families.

The median money income of farm-operator families was only 61 percent as large as that for all families in the United States. Two

---

[4] Ernest W. Grove, "Income of Farm-Operator Families in 1949," in U. S. Dept. of Commerce and U. S. Dept. of Agriculture, *Farms and Farm People, A Special Cooperative Report*, June 1953, pp. 23–44.

explanatory comments should be emphasized. First, this comparison reflects only money incomes. No estimate of nonmoney income has been included, and this is more important on farms than in cities. Value of housing, of farm-raised food, and of other items that must be purchased in urban communities would raise farm incomes if they were included. The second comment relates to the somewhat higher prices for many commodities that prevail in cities as compared with prices in rural areas. The farmer's dollar has more purchasing power. But adjustments for these two factors would still leave urban incomes higher than farm incomes.

Average family incomes by economic classes and percentage of nonfarm incomes are shown in table 9-2. It is evident from these data

TABLE **9-2.**—AVERAGE FAMILY MONEY INCOME FOR FARM-OPERATOR FAMILIES AND THE PERCENTAGE FROM SUPPLEMENTARY NONFARM SOURCES BY ECONOMIC CLASSES, UNITED STATES, 1949

Economic class	Operator family income	Percentage of family income from	
		Nonfarm	Farm [1]
	Dollars	*Percent*	*Percent*
All farms..............	2,650	40	60
Commercial farms...........	2,815	26	74
Class I.................	10,200	13	87
Class II.................	5,600	16	84
Class III................	3,700	18	82
Class IV.................	2,500	30	70
Class V.................	1,900	48	52
Class VI................	975	44	56
Noncommercial farms [2].......	2,260	83	17
Part-time...............	2,400	82	18
Residential..............	2,175	84	16

[1] Includes self-employment income of farm operator from nonfarm business or professional practice, received mainly by operators of part-time and residential farms.
[2] Excluding "unusual" farms to which family income data are not generally applicable.
Source: U. S. Dept. of Commerce and U. S. Dept. of Agriculture, *Farms and Farm People, A Special Cooperative Report*, June 1953, pp. 28 and 30.

that despite whatever shortcomings they may have, average net money income differences between economic classes are much less than one might expect from the gross sales of farm products. The small-scale farms in class VI and some of those in class V have lower incomes, but there is little difference in the level of net family incomes between farms in the class IV, class V, part-time, and residential groups. Further, the elevation of incomes in classes I, II, and III is less than one might suppose.

Nonfarm income includes all nonfarm earnings except the operators' self-employment earnings from nonfarm business or professional practice which were included in farm earnings. To the extent that these enter into the picture the percentages of nonfarm family incomes shown are underestimates.

Nonfarm income makes up more than 80 percent of the money income on part-time and residential farms, but the matter does not end there. Throughout the range of size classes nonfarm income adds materially to the farm family's income. About 40 percent of all farm operators and 27 percent of commercial farm operators reported working off their farms in 1949. Those who worked off the farm 100 days or more made up 23 percent of all farm operators and 9 percent of the commercial farm operators.

For all commercial farms, 26 percent of all family money income came from off-farm sources. Even on class I farms this amounts to 13 percent, and on class V farms it runs to 48 percent. The measure of farm income used is net in the sense that farm expenses have been deducted from gross farm sales to get a figure more nearly comparable with urban incomes.

Color and race in agriculture

Although the race question in the United States is rooted in agriculture, it has long since ceased to be solely an agricultural problem. But in agriculture, problems associated with color and race are found chiefly in the South and in a few smaller areas elsewhere. Statistics from the 1950 Census of Agriculture on these matters are limited to number of farms, land in farms, land use, and a few other items. Many of the data are for the Southern States only.

Indians and some other races are represented in agriculture in small numbers, but Negroes make up most of the nonwhite agricultural population. Percentages of Negroes, other nonwhites (Indians, Japanese, Chinese, and others), and whites in the total of farm operators in the United States in 1930, 1940, and 1950 are given in the accompanying tabulation.

	1930	1940	1950
	Percent	Percent	Percent
Negroes	14.0	11.2	10.4
Other nonwhite	0.6	0.6	0.4
White	85.4	88.2	89.2
Total	100.0	100.0	100.0

The decreasing proportion of Negro farm operators is partly a reflection of certain complex changes in the economy that have involved a very considerable movement of Negroes from rural areas of the South into industrial centers of the Nation. Between 1940 and 1950, for example, the percentage of nonwhites in the United States classified as urban by the Census of Population rose from 47.9 to 58.8. Nonwhites classified as rural farm fell from 35.3 to 21.2 percent, and rural nonfarm rose from 16.7 to 20.1 percent. For the first time in our history, nonwhites and whites are divided between urban and rural segments in almost the same proportions.[5] But more of the nonwhites in the rural part are on farms.

This great shift in population has resulted primarily from the pull of better urban economic opportunities; it has undoubtedly improved the average economic status of the nonwhite population considerably.

The special southern orientation of the racial problem can be illustrated by a few comparisons. The South had a little less than a third of the total United States population in 1950, but it had about two-thirds of the nonwhite population. Or one may say that nonwhites made up 10.5 percent of the total population of the United States and 21.9 percent of the population of the South.

Some 21.2 percent of the nonwhite population of the United States were living on farms in 1950. In the South this percentage was 30.5. By way of comparison, 14.6 percent of the white population of the United States and 23.7 percent of that of the South were on farms.

Despite the recent shift of population away from farms in the South, a special concentration of nonwhites remains in the region and on farms. Those who stayed in agriculture may not have improved their economic position as much as those who left. Some who shifted from cropper to wage status, as mechanization took place in parts of the Cotton Belt, are probably better off. But too many of the nonwhites who remain on farms are still in the very low income groups.

For the country as a whole in 1950, 30 percent of the population in nonwhite farm-operator households was found in economic class VI, as compared with about 10 percent for white farm-operator households (table 9-3). That the problem is partly regional and not altogether racial is shown by corresponding percentages for the South—30.3 percent for nonwhite and 15.5 percent for white farm-operator households. The pressure of population on farm resources is relatively great for both white and nonwhite people in the South. Therefore, instead of having three times as high a percentage of farm people in the lowest economic class, nonwhites in the South have only twice as high a percentage as whites.

The low-income problem in the South, especially, arises primarily from the low-resource base. The difficulty is not restricted to nonwhites; but it must be admitted that the problem affects a larger proportion of the nonwhite population. The ultimate solution lies partly in further migration toward urban opportunities as they become avail-

---

[5] These comparisons are on the basis of the old urban definition, as data for the new urban definition are available for this breakdown only for 1950.

Table 9-3.—Percentage of Population in Farm-Operator Households by Color and Economic Class of Farm, United States, 1950

Economic class	United States		South	
	White	Nonwhite	White	Nonwhite
	Percent	*Percent*	*Percent*	*Percent*
All farms	100.0	100.0	100.0	100.0
Commercial farms	70.4	70.4	60.9	70.3
Classes I and II	10.5	0.7	3.9	0.6
Class III	15.9	2.6	7.1	2.5
Class IV	18.2	11.7	15.1	11.2
Class V	16.0	25.4	19.3	25.7
Class VI	9.8	30.0	15.5	30.3
Noncommercial farms	29.6	29.6	39.1	29.7
Part-time and unusual	12.1	9.0	14.4	9.1
Residential	17.5	20.6	24.7	20.6

Source: U. S. Dept. of Commerce and U. S. Dept. of Agriculture, *Farms and Farm People, A Special Cooperative Report*, June 1953, p. 56.

able and in a gradual reorientation of types of farming that will make possible more resources and larger incomes per farm unit.

Farm labor

We looked at farm labor briefly in Chapter 3 as one of the three members of the triad of resources used in farm production. Now let us consider it from the viewpoint of the people in the labor force.

The bulk of the labor used on our farms is supplied by the farm operator and his family. The fact that family-scale units comprise most of the farms makes this inevitable. The 1950 annual averages of total numbers of workers on farms, taken from the Agricultural Marketing Service revised series on farm employment, are given in the accompanying tabulation.

	Thousands	*Percent*
Family workers	7,252	78
Hired workers	2,090	22
Total family and hired	9,342	100

Thus nearly four-fifths of the farm workers are members of farm operators' families. A considerable number of the regular hired workers are sons of neighboring farm families; others are members of nonfarm families in the same communities whose social and economic status approaches that of tenant farmers. The most disturbing problems arise in the group of seasonal hired workers.

Numbers of seasonal hired workers vary tremendously during the year. The total number of different persons involved in recent years has been estimated as about 3 million, of whom approximately a third, or 1 million, are migratory.[6] It is not possible to be certain about the total number of persons in the families of these itinerant workers. In some classes of migratory workers, whole families are employed in harvesting operations. Of the total number of migratory workers, domestic migrants represent about half. The other half is made up of a small number of British West Indians and Puerto Ricans and a large number of Mexicans, partly under legal contract and partly not.

Seasonal workers who are not migratory are more fortunate in that they live settled lives and for the most part either have other employment or are parts of families with members otherwise employed, so that their annual incomes may be reasonably good.

The story of the migratory workers, therefore, plumbs a depth of human employment experience and living conditions which reaches well below accepted American standards. Their way of life raises serious social questions for the communities in which they work and for those to which they return in winter. Like nomadic groups elsewhere, they do not reach desirable levels in respect to education, sanitation, and other matters of broad public concern.

But this problem must be kept in perspective. From the viewpoint of all farm work, migratory workers represent less than 5 percent of the man-days of work on farms. They are employed on only about 2 percent of the Nation's farms. But they perform essential work for producers of certain specialized crops with heavy peak loads, especially at harvest. And, as pointed out above, they represent a difficult social problem.

Progress in solving this nomadism is taking place at both ends of the problem. Urban employment opportunities will gradually furnish a means of more settled existence. On the farm, increasing mechanization of some crops is reducing peak loads and a more diversified agricultural system in other instances will provide more continuous employment. Mechanization of sugar beet production has already gone far enough to reduce greatly the need for seasonal labor. Machines for thinning, topping, and loading of sugar beets have helped to bring labor requirements for sugar beets into line with those for other crops that have been mechanized.[7] Mechanization of cotton, wheat, rice, and corn production also has reduced seasonal harvest labor needs. There is less prospect of labor-saving improvements for fruit, vegetables, and tobacco, and these categories include many crops for which there is a long-time upward trend in consumption and production. As much of

6 *Migratory Labor in American Agriculture,* Report of the President's Commission on Migratory Labor, 1951, Washington, D. C.

7 See for example the cooperative BAE-Colorado study by Harry G. Sitler and R. T. Burdick, "The Economics of Sugar Beet Mechanization," *Colorado Agr. Expt. Sta. Bul. 411A,* July 1953.

the remaining seasonal labor is used on these crops, progress in reducing peak loads of labor may be less rapid from now on.

Dispersion of homes and community centers

In 1950 the average distance from the farm to the nearest trading center was 6 miles, and 79 percent of all farms in the United States were less than 10 miles from such a center. About two-thirds of all farm homes were within 0.2 miles of an all-weather road. At a speed of 30 miles an hour nearly all farmers on all-weather roads could reach the nearest trading center in 20 minutes by automobile. A little more time and a little more distance would take most of them to a fair-sized city. Many people in cities consume more time in getting about to work, to trade, and to amusements than do farmers. Dispersion no longer means isolation from community activities.

Location of farmsteads on farms instead of in villages as in many other lands is an important element in farm-operating efficiency in the United States. Many early colonial settlements were of the village type. Some religious groups have elected to maintain a village pattern, the Mormons most successfully. But the diffused pattern of settlement was the rule once the Indian menace was over and migration passed the Appalachian barrier. Except in New England and a few other places where the local government units did not separate country from city, the scattered pattern long tended to keep country and town people in separate compartments. Transportation and communication have since modified this situation.

Early rural community centers grew up around a trading center, a church, a school, or some combination of them. Probably the strongest cohesive forces today in the mainly rural communities are schools and trading facilities. Religious and recreational groupings tend to grow up around these primary forces. Emerging urbanization means that in more and more communities farming interests are only one part of the commercial interests of a city that was once mainly a rural town.

Age and natural increase

The age composition of farm people differs from that of urban people in having relatively more of both younger and older people. The difference is greatest among those below 20 years of age. Higher fertility and migration of working age people to urban communities are the main reasons.

The tremendous rise in birthrates during the 1940's was most marked in the urban population; it has tended to reduce urban-rural differentials in fertility. But the number of children under 5 per 1,000 women 15 to 49 years of age remained greater for the farm population than for either the rural-nonfarm or urban population groups in 1950. The ratios were 521, 507, and 372, respectively. Even the urban ratio was more than sufficient to reproduce the urban population with expected mortality. The high farm birthrate means that an important part of the young people from farms must continue to look forward to occupations off the farm. It has been estimated that approximately 168 boys in farm-operator households will reach age 20 in the 1950's for every 100 expected deaths or retirement among men 20 to 64 years of age.[8] This is without regard to further change in farm population, which has followed an average downtrend of nearly 1 percent per year. If this further factor is taken into account, apparently almost half of the young men growing up on farms should look forward to training themselves for urban work opportunities. A somewhat larger proportion of the young women will move away from farm life, and some will return after a few years to be farm wives.

The relatively large number of dependent young and old on farms means that working-age groups on farms bear a disproportionate share of the cost of providing suitable education for the young and retirement facilities for the old. This is the basic reason for sharing these costs over a wider area. Local taxation which in the past carried the major part of the cost of education does not provide a fair sharing of the load. A rough statistical measure of the relative burden has been computed in terms of a "dependency ratio." This is simply the ratio of the number of persons under 15 and over 70 to the number 20 to 64 years of age. These ratios for the several population groups compared with the median money incomes of families and unrelated individuals are given in the accompanying tabulation. The farm population has a dependency

	Dependency ratio	Median money income
United States	54.7	$2,619
Urban	46.6	2,970
Rural nonfarm	64.4	2,186
Farm	75.1	1,567
Farm-operator household	72.5	1,867

ratio half again as large as the urban, but with a considerably lower median cash income.

The age structure of the farm population differs appreciably among economic classes of farms. The age structure for class I and class II farms (large-scale and large family-scale farms) resembles the urban age distribution in the upper age range. But many elderly people from these higher-income farms leave the farm population by retiring to small towns and urban communities. Some move to smaller farms within the area and are then counted in other economic classes. The

---

8 Helen R. White, "Population in Farm-Operator Households," in U. S. Dept. of Commerce and U. S. Dept. of Agriculture, *Farms and Farm People, A Special Cooperative Report,* June 1953, pp. 45–64.

retired Iowa farmers in southern California are not counted in the farm population unless they have reentered farming.   In the economic classes with lower incomes the proportion of older persons remaining on farms is higher because they never accumulate enough to retire.   Economic class VI farms have 11.5 percent of their population 65 years or older as compared with 7.8 percent on all farms.   Part-time farms have less and residential farms more than the average percentage of older persons.

Regional differences in age are most significant as between the South and the rest of the country.   Because of higher fertility, higher mortality, and greater net losses through migration after childhood, farm-operator households are younger in the South than elsewhere.   The median age in April 1950 was 24.1 years in the South and 29.9 in the North and West combined.   The same factors that make for lower median age account for higher dependency ratios in the South.

Sex composition.   The farm population contains a larger proportion of males than females and more than other segments of the population. The proportions for April 1950 are given in the accompanying tabulation.

	Number o males per 100 females
United States	98.6
Urban	94.6
Rural nonfarm	103.6
Farm	110.1

Farms offer more job opportunities for men than for women.   The greater part of farm labor is male.   Farm women must go to the city to find work as clerks, stenographers, factory employees, and at other tasks more suited to their abilities and desires.   Examination of the accompanying tabulation of sex ratios by economic classes provides

	Males per 100 females 14 years and older in farm-operator households
All farms	112.1
Commercial farms	115.3
Classes I and II	125.7
Class III	120.2
Class IV	115.9
Class V	112.3
Class VI	106.7
Noncommercial farms	104.6
Part-time and unusual	107.6
Residential	102.7

further evidence.   The larger farms on which more labor is hired have the highest proportion of men.

The salient features of farm population are thus related to age and sex composition.   The family farm as a business concern is closely associated with a married operator.   But the farm does not provide jobs for more than about half of the farm children after they grow up. Dependency costs thus fall more heavily on the farm working-age population than upon other occupational groups in the whole population. This burden is especially heavy in the case of low-production farms in certain areas in the South.

Mobility of farm people

Mobility is a doubled-edged concept. To the extent that mobility contributes to flexibility in working out economic and social adjustments so that resources are used more adequately and living is improved, mobility is a good thing. But mobility that merely means too rapid a change from farm to farm or from job to job may be an index of insecurity and instability in economic conditions and in social life.

The average number of years on present farms as reported in the 1950 Census of Agriculture was 13. By classes of tenure it was 16 years for full owners, 14 years for part owners, and 6 years for all tenant operators. Some regional variations occur, but this is the general picture. The crucial difference is that between tenants on the one hand and owners and part owners on the other. Although some part of the high mobility of tenants may be explained by the fact that they are younger, it is also an indication of their relative lack of security. The very high percentage of tenants with shorter than average terms of tenancy is even more disturbing. In the Northwest 50 percent, and in the North Central States 56 percent, of the tenants had been on their farms less than 5 years. In the South and West the proportions were 67 and 65 percent, respectively. Many tenants occupy a farm for only 1 or 2 years. Part of the explanation lies in the differences between tenants and owners in age and experience, which in turn are related to the time needed to accumulate capital and other factors associated with climbing the tenure ladder. In 1950 all tenants averaged 40.9 and all owners averaged 51.0 years of age, a difference of 10 years.

Mobility as a means of adjustment. A desirable kind of mobility is that which helps to attain an improved situation either on or off the farm. To this kind of mobility modern means of communication and travel have contributed greatly. Education in both the formal and the informal sense has made itself felt too.

Fifty years ago, a farm was in a separate world with infrequent communication with the "outside." The technology of communication has changed all this. Rural free delivery of mail, automobiles and improved highways, telephones, radios, television sets, and other devices keep farmers in better touch with main events than many city people. Some of the same forces that have caused rural areas to become more accessible in recent years have made cities more congested and less desirable places to live. As pointed out earlier, about 80 percent of all census farms were less than 10 miles from the "nearest trading center" in 1950 and two-thirds of all farms were on all-weather roads.   Mail is delivered as frequently to farms as to urban residences.   A farmer's wife may walk a few feet farther to the mailbox.   The radio is universal. Television reaches rural areas to almost the same extent as urban areas. Eventual coverage will differ little.

Farmers do fall short in one respect.   In 1950, telephones were reported in only a third of the farm homes; but this lack is likely to be rapidly repaired under Rural Electrification Administration stimulus and with the aid of recent technological improvements that have reduced installation costs.   Automobiles were found on 60 percent of all farms and if farm trucks are taken into account, three-fourths of all farmers had power wheeling available.   A few farmers even go to town on rubber-tired tractors.

All these devices increase contacts and communication and permit people to learn about opportunities.   They are the essential means for keeping abreast of events and for obtaining information about possible economic adjustments.

Education

The formal education of those who live on farms lags somewhat behind that of rural-nonfarm and urban groups.   But more significant is the rapid progress that is made from decade to decade.   The proportion of farm persons 25 to 34 years of age in 1950 who had completed elementary school was nearly 50 percent greater, and the proportion of those who had completed high school was 3 times as great as the corresponding proportion of those 55 years of age and older (table 9-4).

TABLE 9-4.—PERCENTAGE WHO HAD COMPLETED ELEMENTARY SCHOOL, HIGH SCHOOL, AND COLLEGE, BY SELECTED AGE GROUPS AND BY AREA OF RESIDENCE, 1950

Age and residence	Schooling completed [1]		
	Elementary school	High school	College
	Percent	Percent	Percent
25–34 years:			
Urban	87	54	9
Rural nonfarm	78	42	5
Farm	70	31	2
55 years and over:			
Urban	59	22	5
Rural nonfarm	53	15	3
Farm	48	10	2

[1] Elementary school, 8 years; high school, 4 years; college, 4 years.   Each category includes all who had completed the indicated years or more.

Among young adults 25 to 34 years old, 70 percent of those living on farms had completed elementary school in 1950 as compared with 78 percent in rural-nonfarm areas and 87 percent in urban areas. The elementary picture is thus not greatly different. But less than a third of the same age groups living on farms had completed high school as compared with more than two-fifths of those in the rural-nonfarm group and more than half of those in urban areas. These data, significant as they are, do not represent the real difference in educational opportunities available to farm people. Selective migration at this age has already caused many of those with high educational attainments to move from farm to city jobs.[9] Education contributes to successful mobility, helping young people to prepare for nonfarm jobs and in making them more aware of such opportunities.

How important education may be for those who stay on the farm but supplement their income by work off the farm is suggested by the direct association between educational attainment and off-farm work. Only a fifth of those farm operators who did not complete elementary school reported working off the farm 100 days or more. This compares with a fourth of those completing elementary school and a third of those completing high school.[10]

Educational characteristics of farm operators are becoming significant in present-day farming. Those who have had college experience are now numerous enough to be visible in the statistics. In the country as a whole, 5.6 percent of all farm operators have had 1 or more years of college; for farmers in classes I and II the percentage is 14.1, or about 1 farmer in 7. Those with 4 years or more of college comprise 2 percent of all farmers and 4.7 percent of farmers in classes I and II. Young men who have completed college presumably have a wider choice of future occupations before them, and it is significant that so many have chosen farming.

Farm homes and equipment [11]

Home is more than four walls enclosing a collection of automatic gadgets. But the content of farm living is closely associated with the kind of farmhouse and the facilities it contains for making life and work in the home more pleasant. Farm homes are frequently more favorably situated with respect to light, air, and general outlook than

9 The 1950 Census practice of counting college students where they were attending college rather than in their parental homes enters here, too; for this means that young people from farms who are away at college are not counted in the farm population.

10 Jackson V. McElveen, "Low-Production Farms and the Low-Income Problem in Agriculture," in U. S. Dept. of Commerce and U. S. Dept. of Agriculture, *Farms and Farm People, A Special Cooperative Report,* June 1953, pp. 9–21—see especially p. 20.

11 For background materials see Barbara B. Reagan, "Housing Facilities and Equipment and Home Production Practices of Farm-Operator Families," in U. S. Dept. of Commerce and U. S. Dept. of Agriculture, *Farms and Farm People, A Special Cooperative Report,* June 1953, pp. 65–98.

city homes. But they are not always so well provided with the items of physical equipment that add to good living and reduce household drudgery. This situation has changed rapidly, but further improvement is to be desired. Progress has been less rapid in this area than in the farm business itself, partly because these improvements compete with long-term income-producing farm investments. In many instances, construction, remodeling, and new equipment would require funds that appear to be needed for increasing farm income.

Electrification marks the greatest advance. Here a veritable revolution has taken place in farm homes in a short space of time (fig. 9-1).

FIGURE 9-1. PERCENTAGE OF FARM OPERATORS REPORTING SPECIFIED FAMILY LIVING ITEMS, UNITED STATES, 1920 TO 1950

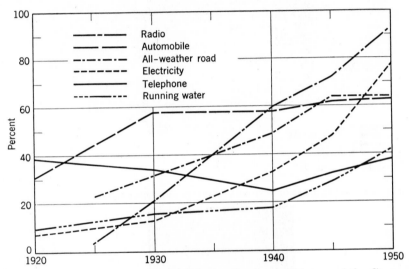

Source: Data are from Agricultural Marketing Service and Bureau of the Census.

Just a few years ago, if a visitor drove down a country road about six in the evening, he'd see just two points of yellowish light at each farmstead. There was an oil lamp in the kitchen; there was an oil lantern bobbing around in the farmyard as the farmer did his chores. . . . Now light bursts from a dozen windows in every house. There's a big bulb at the top of a pole in the barnyard. It makes the barnyard clear as day. Lights switch on in the dairy barn, in the chicken house, at the corncrib.[12]

Not only has the darkness of centuries been banished, but farm housewives now have many labor-saving devices. Some 78 percent of all farmhouses were electrified by 1950, and the figure has since risen to nearly 90 percent (fig. 9-2). This compares with about 10 percent in 1935. Counts of electrical appliances of various kinds show that

---

[12] Donald R. Murphy, "Winter on the Farm Is Cozier," *The New York Times Magazine*, Feb. 7, 1954.

farm families have taken rapid advantage of electric power. Three-fourths of those with electricity had electric washing machines in 1950, 9 in 10 had mechanical refrigerators, and nearly all had radios (table 9-5).

FIGURE 9-2. FARMS AND ELECTRICITY, PERCENTAGE OF FARMS RECEIVING CENTRAL STATION SERVICE

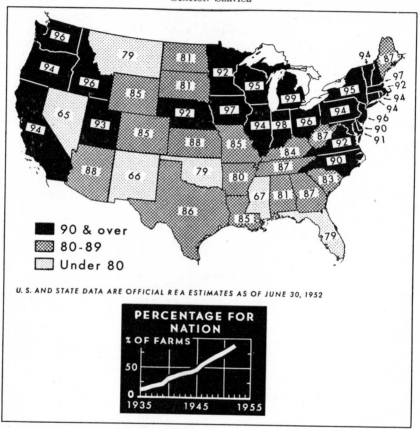

Source: Agricultural Marketing Service.

But a similar revolution in plumbing and heating will be necessary to bring the farm family up to parity with urban families in home conveniences. Although electricity now makes water under pressure practical, adequate plumbing and the related kitchen and bathroom facilities that depend on running water are lacking in too many farm homes. In 1950, less than a third of farm-operator homes had installed a bathtub or a shower or an indoor flush toilet. As many as 42 percent lacked kitchen sinks, and 57 percent did not have piped running water in the house. Much but not all the lack is on class V and class VI farms. For example, more than half of the class III farms did not have bathroom facilities.

TABLE 9-5.—HOUSING CHARACTERISTICS AND EQUIPMENT OF FARM-OPERATOR DWELLING UNITS, UNITED STATES AND REGIONS, 1950

Characteristic	United States	North and West	South
	Percent	Percent	Percent
Condition:			
Not dilapidated..	84	93	75
Dilapidated..	16	7	25
Size:			
1 or 2 rooms...	4	3	5
3 or 4 rooms...	29	17	41
5 or 6 rooms...	38	38	39
7 or more rooms..	29	42	15
Year built: [1]			
1945 or later..	9	5	14
1940 to 1944...	6	3	9
1930 to 1939...	14	9	20
1920 to 1929...	14	13	17
1919 or earlier..	57	70	40
Water supply:			
Hot and cold piped running water inside structure.............	31	46	18
Cold piped running water inside structure....................	12	13	11
No piped running water inside structure......................	57	41	71
Plumbing facilities:			
Flush toilet inside structure..............................	30	42	18
Installed bathtub or shower..............................	33	45	21
Kitchen sink [1]...	58	77	37
Refrigerator: [1]			
Mechanical..	66	79	53
Ice...	12	5	18
Other or none...	22	16	29
Cooking fuel: [1]			
Coal or wood..	49	37	62
Liquid fuel..	8	6	9
Gas or electricity......................................	42	56	27
Other or none...	1	1	2

[1] Statistics based on a 20-percent sample.

Source: U. S. Dept. of Commerce and U. S. Dept. of Agriculture, *Farms and Farm People, A Special Cooperative Report*, June 1953, p. 68.

The contrast with electrification is so startling that one seeks for an explanation. Rural electrification has advanced rapidly in recent years, mainly because of the establishment of the Rural Electrification Administration. Once a farm home is wired for electricity, the provision of specialized appliances is only a matter of time. Acquisition is expedited by the fact that electric appliances can be bought individually, as funds are available. The financing problem is thus greatly simplified.

Plumbing facilities usually mean a much larger initial outlay, and this is often an insuperable barrier. A bathroom may require a major reconstruction job on the house to provide the running water and to install central heating sufficient to protect against winter freezing. All this is more expensive than wiring a house for electricity. Outdoor provision for an adequate water supply and waste disposal may also require a major outlay.

No doubt the costs of installing plumbing in farmhouses could be reduced considerably if as much thought and effort were directed to the problem as has gone into the electrification field. If new techniques

FIGURE 9-3. RUNNING WATER IN FARM HOUSES, PERCENTAGE OF DWELLING UNITS

[Includes vacant and seasonal units]

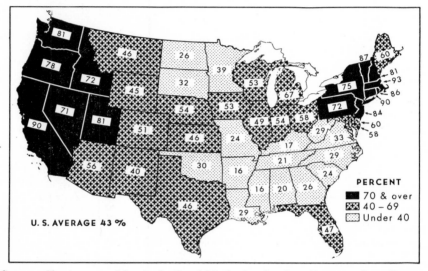

Source: Chart prepared by Agricultural Marketing Service. Data are from Bureau of the Census.

and reduction of costs could be introduced into the plumbing business, progress could be fairly rapid. But unless this can be done, there is doubt about the rate of progress that can be made on lower-income farms. Farm families with limited income will choose other uses for their money. The geographic distribution of the problem is illustrated in fig. 9-3. In 1950 the Northeast and the West had the highest percentages of farm dwellings with piped running water.

Housing. This brings us to farm dwellings. In the background is the fact that farm population has been shrinking as contrasted with expanding urban population. This situation alone would tend to keep farm homes older. More than half (57 percent) of the farm-operator dwelling units in 1950 were more than 30 years old, and only 9 percent had been built in the last 5 years. Of course, age is not a good measure of the condition or character of housing, and the Census of Housing asked a question about dilapidation.[13]   Answers to this question indicated that 16 percent of all farm-operator dwellings were dilapidated, 7 percent in the North and West and about 25 percent in the South. Houses in the North and West were larger, averaging 5 to 6 rooms as compared with 3 to 4 in the South.

Housing for farm operators was in somewhat better shape than that for year-round hired workers and considerably better than for seasonal workers.   Data on vacant houses (occupied seasonally) and for other-than-operator houses on farms, indicated inferior condition.   Houses occupied by year-round farm workers, although less modern than those of employers, were comparable with homes on smaller farms in the same areas.

Housing on low-production farms.   Houses on farms in classes V and VI were inferior to those on farms in classes I to IV.   This was especially the case on class VI farms where two-thirds of the family money incomes were less than $1,000.   Farms in these classes are more highly concentrated in the South and in cotton and tobacco areas.   In the South, fewer than 15 percent of the class VI farms had running water piped into the dwelling or used electricity or gas for cooking. Very few had telephones and about a third of the dwellings were classed as dilapidated.   But 60 percent had electricity for lighting.

Part-time and residential farms.   Part-time and residential farms have considerably better housing than farms in classes V and VI.   Most of these families have higher family incomes, and this is reflected in their housing facilities.   Many of the part-time and residential farms are nearer urban centers; the families participate to a greater extent in the advantages of schools, roads, and other public services.

Home food production practices.   One advantage of a farm is the possibility of raising a garden and keeping some livestock for home consumption.   Not all farm-operator families follow this pattern.   But 70 percent of those in the North and West and 80 percent of those in the South raised vegetables for home use in 1949.   Slightly higher percentages kept chickens, and about two-thirds slaughtered some meat animals, most frequently hogs.   About three-fourths of the Northerners and two-thirds of the Southerners produced some milk.

Production of food for home use is related to economic class of farms in the South.   The proportion of those with gardens, chickens, and home-produced meat increased as the size of the farm business decreased. Milk cows, on the other hand, were less frequent on the smaller farms. In the North and West, medium-sized farms had the largest proportion with home-produced food.

---

13 A dwelling unit was reported as dilapidated when it had serious deficiencies, was run-down or neglected, or was of inadequate original construction so that it did not provide adequate shelter against the elements or endangered the safety of the occupants. Specific criteria were set up for appraising these points.

Rural health and medical care

Farm people have been handicapped in the matter of health and medical services more than have city people. Rural isolation and the distinct urban orientation of health facilities have long been stubborn barriers to improvement. The isolation factor has been largely overcome, but urban orientation of doctors and hospitals has increased. There are still major problems to be overcome before farm people will have full parity in health services.

Against this background and in the light of an increasing public awareness of the problem, new health programs will be instituted in time. Whatever direction these programs take, they are likely to improve the relative position of rural areas with respect to the services of physicians, hospitals, and preventive medicine.

Hospitals are probably the central keys to the distribution of physicians. These "workshops" bring with them auxiliary services that not only make the doctor more effective but also increase his chances of getting a reasonably good income. The contemporary emphasis on construction of hospitals is therefore well placed.

The high rejection rates of farm youth among the selective service registrants during World War II have aroused much discussion (table 9-6). The high over-all rate is perhaps more significant, but the still

TABLE 9-6.—REJECTION RATES PER 100 SELECTIVE SERVICE REGISTRANTS EXAMINED IN THE UNITED STATES BY OCCUPATION, APRIL 1, 1942, TO DECEMBER 31, 1943

Occupational group	Rate per 100 registrants
All occupations	42.6
Domestic service workers	59.6
Emergency workers and unemployed	56.5
Farmers and farm managers	56.4
Farm laborers and foremen	52.8
Service workers, except domestic and protective	49.1
Laborers, except farm and mine	46.6
Proprietors, managers, and officials, except farm	46.4
Protective service workers	42.7
Professional and semiprofessional	42.2
Craftsmen, foremen, and kindred workers	40.7
Clerical, sales, and kindred workers	37.5
Operatives and kindred workers	37.2
Students	25.7
Others	44.5

Source: "Physical Examinations of Selective Service Registrants During Wartime," *Selective Service System, Medical Statistics Bul. 3,* 1944, table 3, p. 12.

higher rate for farm persons has called for some soul searching. Further analysis of the crude rejection rates has shown that if allowance could be made for physical defects apart from mental and educational defects, rural and farm rates would be smaller than those for nonagricultural occupations.[14] The special rural assets of fresh air and sunshine appear to give farmers a slight edge, so far as physical condition is concerned. Yet the over-all 42.6 percent rejection rate indicates that the problem of health improvement is a major one in both city and country.

Reflections

The farm family, like its city cousin, is evolving toward the small, single-generation type of family—one that is more independent and mobile than the larger kinship groups of the past. But under farm conditions this evolution has elements of stability and strength that are lacking in the city. The blend of working and living and the closer cooperation between members of the farm family make it a more cohesive unit than its city counterpart. The quieter harmony of biological production processes and the less crowded atmosphere of the country are values that are difficult to match in the more feverish life of the city. The contribution of the farm families to Western civilization may well be out of proportion to their apparent place in the scheme of things. Part-time farming, residential farming, and country residential living may supply rural values to many who must work in cities.

Most of the labor on farms is that of the operator and his family, but hired workers account for nearly a fifth of the total number of farm workers. Living among the less-advantaged hired farm workers, and especially among some migratory workers, fails to reach desirable levels. Progress is being made, but much remains to be done, both for ethical reasons and from the viewpoint of such matters as public health and sanitation.

The transfer of land and other resources between generations is more intricate on the farm than elsewhere. It is a problem that has not been fully solved in a way that is both equitable to the individuals immediately concerned and most productive for society. This problem is closely related to that of assistance to young farmers in getting started in business.

Age composition of population on farms as contrasted with that of the urban sector, shows a heavier load of younger and older people relative to working-age groups. As a result the burden of local taxation and support of community services falls more heavily on farmers.

More men than women are employed in agriculture, and this is reflected in the sex composition of the farm population, which has relatively more males. In view of the greater pull of urban employment

14 Mapheus Smith, "Occupational Differentials in Physical Status," *American Sociological Review,* Feb. 1948, pp. 72–82.

opportunities for women, it is surprising that the differences are not greater. Possibly underemployment of women on farms is still greater than that of men. More job opportunities for women in nearby communities might be desirable.

All the media of transportation and communication have contributed to informal education and to mobility of farm people. Great progress has been made in formal education, too, but this is probably the area in which most remains to be accomplished. Formal education is the most economical way in which young men and women can uncover their latent abilities and prepare for opportunities both at home and away from home.

In the physical equipment for farm living, the basic problem today turns around housing and adequate provision for plumbing and heating. Medical and health facilities in rural areas also will require attention before farm people can attain parity in living conditions.

CHAPTER 10

CHANGES AND STRUCTURAL STRAIN

As those who have read the earlier chapters are aware, the intent in this book is neither to forecast the future nor to propose courses of action. The leading objective is to help us televise new agricultural pictures for our mental screens so that we may see more truly. The task of refilming is not finished until we can look at the structure in its entirety. One who reviews the whole of agriculture in this way and reflects on how it has changed during the years must conclude that the midcentury status of farms and farm people reveals marked improvement. Farms are more efficient, businesslike, and productive than they were in 1900. Farm people lead more satisfying lives today than formerly. The disparities between farm and city ways of life have shrunk perceptibly. Lines of communication have been built across the chasm of former separation. Rural and urban people now share a common culture to a degree unknown perhaps in any other time or place.

But an observer who examines the structure of a building would be remiss in his duty if he failed to report evidence of wear and damage. Even though the building may be strong, cracks in the walls, leaks in the roof, faults in the foundation, and other indicators of trouble in the making should be noted. Before a statistician can venture to forecast outcomes, before a social architect can propose remedies, the weaknesses in the structure must be known.

The immediate task in this chapter, therefore, is to appraise the stresses and strains, the pressure points, and the tensions that beset agriculture. Many, and perhaps most of them, are associated with change and the inevitable adjustments that grow out of change. Some of them arise from a growing awareness of disparities of long standing. The old proverb says that "ignorance is bliss." And as information replaces ignorance bliss departs and stress appears. Thus arises the not uncommon paradox of strain and strife in the midst of progressive improvement.

In the world context, increasing awareness on the part of those in underdeveloped countries of what people elsewhere enjoy is one of the great explosive forces of our time. Awakening to the knowledge that better things are possible may be a disturbing stimulant. So also, on the national scene, increasing comprehension of the remaining disparities between rural and urban opportunities results in new tensions that press for attention.

At bottom, it is change itself that brings stress to the structure. Change takes many outward forms. There are the repeated ebbs and flows of the business cycle, the episodic breaks of war, the long-term secular trends that fade into historical epochs. But, underneath the statistical surface, economic and social conditions continually shift and evolve. In constructing a picture of the current structure of agriculture and its background, it is the fact of change and further transformation that stands out.

Structure implies a certain form and rigidity. Even though the structure changes, it does so unevenly. Some institutions are readily malleable, others warp, buckle, and break. Questions arise as to how well the structure meets the demands on it, how it stands the strain of continuous pressure, how it works out inevitable adjustments.

The broad outline of the structure of agriculture that has emerged has a central core of several million competing commercial farms. At one side are the noncommercial farms, the part-time and residential farms, whose operators and families live in the country but find most of their income elsewhere. Surrounding the central core of commercial farms, is an outer envelope of related group interests—farm organizations, cooperatives, independent private businesses, and government agencies. From the viewpoint of economic-decision making, the structure is intricate. Perhaps most business decisions are made by farmers independently. But many overriding background decisions are made by those who operate the various levers of the group machinery.

One of the greatest forms of strain in the whole business structure of agriculture is related to the lack of synchronization between the separated areas of decision-making with respect to the direction of production and the use of resources. Most conspicuous are problems related to withdrawal of resources from areas of low marginal returns and their reassignment to other areas of higher returns, either inside or outside agriculture.

Reallocation of resources used in agriculture is at best cumbersome and difficult, especially when it involves the termination or reduction of productive activity that affects many farm families. It is easy to talk about the need for farm consolidation. But with the existing structure of private enterprise this may involve many personal tragedies before it is accomplished. Family-scale farms lack flexibility as compared with most urban businesses and the space- and time-bound nature of the biological processes contributes to this lack. Development of social control of some elements in production adjustment has added to the strain.

Technology and social decision

An illustration of the over-all difficulty in synchronizing economic decisions arises from technology. New technology is adopted by individual farmers, but their separate decisions to do so cannot take into account the total effect on farm output. Rates of adoption have been accelerated, and competition has forced new techniques into use so rapidly that production often tends to exceed market needs. The primary reason for the availability of new technology is research and experimentation. Agricultural research is heavily government-supported. Society makes a conscious decision to invest resources in the development of new technology.

Research is a peculiar production activity. So far as basic research is concerned, the incidence of its practical application is unpredictable. But much agricultural research is applied research, devoted to specific objectives; and within limits this is a predictable activity. Conscious decision to invest money in a research effort in a particular area is likely to get results in that area. Thus, the stream of new technology that flows from agricultural experiment stations and research laboratories is fed from springs of consciously renewed social decisions.

Extension and information mechanisms that place results of research in the hands of farmers and that help them to follow new practices have also been developed largely at public expense. With these forces tending to produce an expanding flow of production, there has frequently been sustained pressure on market outlets.

The point has been made that "technological advances are unlikely to be introduced in agricultural production unless or until there is economic incentive to do so."[1] Although this is true in the individual sense, it overlooks the fundamental fact that what is good for individual farm producers is frequently bad for the agricultural industry as a whole. Furthermore, the rapid rate of adoption of new technology in a period when the economic climate is favorable, as during a war, may leave agriculture with excess capacity for some time thereafter. Storm signals of economic distress do not result in an early movement of resources from agriculture into other lines of production. The structure tends to resist, and strains result. Price supports may avert disaster for a time, but the pressure continues.

This broad situation has been recognized for some time, but the role of technology has only recently been made clear. Only since the great wartime advance in technology in agriculture has its significance

[1] Harry C. Trelogan and Neil W. Johnson, "The Evitability of Technological Advance," *Journal of Farm Economics,* Nov. 1953.

been fully realized. The agricultural recession of the 1920's, which culminated in the depression of the 1930's, resulted from a mixture of causes of which technology was only one. It takes a milieu like that of the 1940's and 1950's to reveal the full stature of technology.

Group interests in agriculture have grappled with the synchronization problem only indirectly. Cooperatives, credit facilities, and farm programs of the government have all helped. But, for the most part, the Nation still depends on the "natural forces" of competition and the attraction of nonfarm alternatives to draw excess resources away from agriculture.

A theory advanced by Schultz and others is that adjustment takes place to best advantage in areas that are in the "main stream" of economic development in an expanding economy.[2] Agriculture in the peripheral or distant segments of such an economy is likely to be locked in the grip of custom and to be necessarily disadvantaged. This is an illuminating theory, but it may represent an oversimplification. Probably even in the main stream, adjustment lags unless greater synchronization is achieved. In the industrial world, production is sometimes brought into alignment by holding back the rate of adoption of new technology until such time as competition may force the issue or until the market expands. It is said that some manufactured articles could be made to last much longer—too long for producers to continue in business. Protection of patents and copyrights is frequently a powerful weapon to check too rapid an expansion in output. Trelogan and Johnson advance the possibility of developing new research findings faster than such new technology can be put into use. They suggest that "in taking into account such a contingency, technical knowledge would be less costly to store and draw upon in the event of war than to store commodities and draw upon stocks."[3]

Few would advocate restriction of the rate of adoption of new technology on the part of farmers or the reduction of social support for basic and applied research. We have too strong a belief in the ultimate beneficence of the social gains that arise from greater efficiency. Too many of the ills of society have been reduced or eliminated in this way. Moreover, it is clear that the economy as a whole benefits from more efficiently produced food and fiber, even though little economic gain accrues to the farmer. As elsewhere, the chief gains from technology are likely to be passed on to other sectors of the economy. But, to be consistent, we must recognize the need for synchronization of effort so that farmers will get part of the benefits. If at one end we have social decision that results in larger output than can be absorbed by the market

---

2 Theodore W. Schultz, *Economic Organization of Agriculture*, McGraw-Hill Book Co., Inc., New York, 1953.

3 Trelogan and Johnson, *loc. cit.*, p. 604.

at remunerative prices to farmers, at the other end we should supplement the private decision making of individual farmers with types of group decision that will help to expand market outlets and assist the movement of resources away from agriculture. Here is an area of great strain.

Some may say that this has been done with agricultural programs that involve price supports, acreage allotments, marketing quotas, and the like. Nearly everyone realizes that these measures ameliorate short-run difficulties but do not get at long-range problems. In some respects they even aggravate the ultimate strain of adjustment by retarding the movement of resources. The agricultural economy has been twice rescued by war and world events from the cumulative strains of production in excess of market needs. But this kind of coincidence cannot be counted on, nor would we wish it to happen. Furthermore, the restrictions imposed by short-range programs—acreage controls, for example—also speed up the rate of adoption of yield-increasing techniques and are in part self-defeating.

Strain outside the main stream. The theory of the main stream of economic development and the disadvantages of being outside the zone of influence of the principal expanding urban areas may help to explain some of the low-income areas in eastern Canada and southern United States. In these areas the economic and social structures and the institutions that support them have been so thoroughly set in the past that they have tended to resist urbanization, even on close approach. Catalytic effects of public schools, service in the Armed Forces, and the spread of good highways and communications are gradually wearing away these barriers, but they still represent real obstacles.

General education and communication work toward bringing the backwaters and eddies into the main stream of social progress. Further expansion of formal education and of communication facilities is probably what is most needed to bring these people into contact with outside alternatives and to help those who remain make the best use of local resources.

Mobility and transfer of resources

The lag between the introduction of new technology and the out-transfer of resources is seen as a major element of strain in the agricultural structure. Improving mobility of resources is one way to overcome this lag. The basic inelasticity of both supply and demand for farm products is responsible for much of the problem. When new technology is applied, output is almost certain to increase unless resources are withdrawn from agriculture. If markets can be expanded, this may permit some increase in output. In a limited number of instances, an improvement may embody a cost-reducing change that may not expand output. For example, an improved machine may reduce a specific labor input or other requirement while leaving output undisturbed. But the more common situation is one in which costs can be reduced only by increasing output unless resources can be transferred.

In the last 50 years, labor resources released from agriculture have furnished a significant segment of the growing labor force in city occupations. At the same time working hours on the farm have been shortened and the farm family has gained leisure. Transfer of labor from farm to city has often gone too slowly, but it has helped to keep farm output from rising still more. The future flow from farm to city must continue because of surplus young people growing up in farm families. But possibilities of labor transfers are now more severely limited than they were in the past, because in most types of farming, the hired labor force has been reduced to a comparatively low level. Further displacement of farm labor by machinery will involve to a much greater extent the release of farm operators and operator families from agriculture. Farm enlargement and the search for nonfarm occupations for displaced operators and their families is a more difficult adjustment, but it is one that must be faced. Obviously, many low-income farms that are already too small will be even more disadvantaged in future unless ways can be found to increase the mobility of farm people.

Political roadblocks and flexible linkage. The political processes in a democratic society are subject to change and evolution along with the economic processes. Here again synchronized timing is a key to smooth transition. A political scientist who observes the contemporary scene cannot fail to note the growth and increasing ascendancy of organized blocs, pressure groups, and other concentrations of power for the purpose of influencing public opinion, legislation, and public administration. This phenomenon reaches across business, labor, agriculture, and all other parts of the economy. The full flowering of such social groupings may not have been foreseen by the Founding Fathers, but the gentlemen who operated committees of correspondence and participated in resistance to the tyranny of British colonial rule were no strangers to the use of organized political pressure.

With the extension of modern communication and the multiplicity of contacts between people in all phases of daily life, no alternative means of focusing public opinion on pertinent issues appears to be feasible. But a serious problem is how to deal with certain faults in the way in which such groups function. Too often a group organized around a specific commodity or interest develops a myopia with respect to the general welfare. Too often becoming firmly wedded to a once-desirable viewpoint, it forms a substantial roadblock to a change in policy or program that is strongly indicated by new circumstances.

Some of this inflexibility apparently arises from imperfections in the social mechanism for transmission of valuations between farmers and the leadership of organized agriculture. Much as in a modern business corporation where the active management that controls the corporation's policies loses close contact with the stockholders, so in some farm organizations there is imperfect linkage between the central management and the constituent membership. Frequently, the leadership may stand to gain more from a particular measure than the rank and file of members. The mere fact that a given farm organization has fought hard for high-level price supports (or for variable price supports) is no guarantee that the rank and file would agree with this position if they thoroughly understood the issues and could vote on the question.

A research study of Michigan farmers' attitudes toward agricultural price-support programs made in 1950 revealed inconsistencies and conflicts in attitudes and raised a question as to whether leaders of farm organizations were correctly appraising their members' opinions.[4] For example, a major inference in recent years has been that farmers are opposed to direct payments. As a rule farm groups have opposed such payments. But sentiment for direct payments as a method of supporting prices of perishable products showed surprising strength in this Michigan study of farmers' choices.

The leading general farm organizations have improved their programs of general education greatly, and in recent years their leaders have attained closer contact with the members. As time goes on they may be more successful in eliminating the short circuits and blocks in their communication lines and they may become more flexible in changing position on issues as economic conditions are modified. As the economic literacy of farmers rises it will become even more essential for the leadership of farm groups to clear their lines for mutual communication. Failure to do so may well result in loss of influence and less effective action.

In the current period of transition from a war and near-war economy to one that is hopefully a more peaceful one, many shifts in agricultural policies and programs may be imperative to prevent inefficient and wasteful use of resources. The practical functioning of the political machinery by which a democracy works out such transitions is of importance to farmers and to all citizens. Periods of profound deadlock between opposing forces are not helpful. Unyielding attitudes, inflexible positions on key issues do not contribute to the art of political compromise, which is as necessary in agriculture as elsewhere if democracy is to function.

---

4 Dale E. Hathaway and Lawrence W. Witt, "Agricultural Policy: Whose Valuations?" *Journal of Farm Economics*, Aug. 1952.

Farm risks and the life perilous

Farming is a hazardous occupation. Its risks to life and limb rank near those of mining and construction work. To the physical dangers are added the economic risks of highly variable earnings, which result from weather hazards and from the fortuitous shocks of general prosperity and recession. All these circumstances are familiar enough to farmers, but they are not always realized by those in other occupations.

Many of the risks in farming are aggravated by the relatively small family-scale operations that are typical. Weather episodes that are comparatively mild aggregate manifestations may strike some individuals devastating blows. Hailstorms, for example, are often freakishly localized. Hazards of this kind can be handled by insurance. Hail insurance is one of the few classes of crop insurance with which private insurance companies have had a measure of success. The Federal Crop Insurance Corporation for some years has tackled the broader crop-insurance risks in an experimental program, both in terms of specific crops and in the form of multiple-crop coverage. In order to avoid the rather great uncertainties of price fluctuations, federal crop insurance has followed a unique method of insuring in physical units of a given crop rather than in dollars. Premiums and indemnities may be paid in dollars, but they are computed in the standard unit of measure for the commodity and converted into cash equivalents.

The perennial interest in insurance proposals of all kinds is an index of the general feeling that risk continues to be a serious problem in agriculture. Price insurance has been suggested as one element in an improved price-support program. It is suggested that a revolving fund or reservoir be established to receive in-payments in periods of high prices and to make out-payments in periods of low prices. In this way, farmers might be able to carry a larger part of their own risks by avoiding the feast and famine situation that so frequently accompanies prosperity and recession.

Whether farming is more risky than formerly might be difficult to prove. But the risks are surely different. Few farmers are injured by runaway horses nowadays, but a good many are hurt in accidents with power machinery. Mechanization has reduced some weather risks by making it possible to complete strategic tasks quickly when a favorable break comes in a long period of bad weather. The work of plant breeders has shown up in higher crop yields, but the general adoption of a single crop variety may leave the way open for a wide attack by disease, as happened with Clinton oats and one race of rust in 1953.

The increased size of the family farm, its greater investment in capital equipment, and the tendency toward specialization in a smaller number of products lead to greater vulnerability to risk factors. When drought strikes or economic storms break, a commercial farmer who operates with a much higher current cash outlay than did his father or grandfather finds it harder to avert catastrophe. If he is free of debt, he may come through a minor recession with little trouble. But tractors do not consume farm-produced fuel, and continued attrition from a cost-price squeeze has a grinding pressure that was formerly unknown.

In the past, social security provisions were less necessary for farm than for urban dwellers. But it is increasingly apparent that farm ownership (the desirable goal) neither provides sufficient protection nor makes enough farm families secure against the risks of old age and personal misfortune. Recent legislation to extend the social security coverage of the old age and survivorship program to more self-employed groups, including farmers, will help to correct this situation.

Parity in education and health

The Nation can better afford to help people make wiser individual choices than to spend money for relieving distress that arises from unfortunate choices. In short, prevention is usually less costly than cure. Adequate provisions for education and health facilities probably stand first among measures that are related to mobility and access to opportunity as well as to general well-being.

Great progress in providing general education and health facilities has taken place in this country in the last generation. But plainly some large inequities in opportunity remain if we can judge from the data cited in Chapter 9. Incomplete education and imperfect health are closely related to the problem of transferring resources and finding nonfarm occupations for underemployed people in areas outside the main stream. Young people who were disadvantaged in these respects did not do well in the Nation's Armed Forces. Nor do they compete effectively in the labor market. The experience of the Armed Forces points up the fact that many individuals are ill prepared for the ordinary battles of life. Achievement of full parity of opportunity by redirection of educational and health goals means more than superficial overhauling of programs in these fields and more than just expenditure of money. The same funds now spent could be more effectively utilized if they were better fitted to the needs of the groups affected by certain disadvantages.

Education of farm youth in all areas and especially in low-income areas should provide for training in a variety of occupations both inside and outside agriculture. More than half the young farm people in areas of surplus population will need to look forward to nonfarm occupations. Secondary schools should keep this fact in the forefront. At the same time, those who wish to remain in farming should have an opportunity to learn the skills that will permit them to do so. Such education need not be conceived on a narrow vocational basis. The folk high schools in Denmark, for example, indicate the success that can be attained through a largely cultural approach.

The problem of retaining young people in agriculture in both high- and low-income areas should be approached on the basis of free and equal choice among alternative economic opportunities. If young people who stay in agriculture are forced to do so because their lack of training permits no other choice, we may well drift toward an under-privileged peasant agriculture.[5]

Beyond the problems of education and training, there is the further Gordian knot of how young people without financial assistance can get started in farming. How do they gain the initial foothold? A visible fault in the existing institutional structure appears at this point. The lower rungs on the old-time agricultural ladder have been knocked out. The distance from the ground to the first rung is too far for many to reach easily. In the old days when less capital was needed, it was easier to get started. Even the hired-worker rung has been almost eliminated by technological displacement of labor. How to replace these missing rungs in some alternative way is the problem. Father-and-son leases and other arrangements for gradually taking over the active management of a farm fit some family situations. But these offer little aid to a young man especially fitted for farming who does not have family help. Sometimes a period of work in a nonfarm occupation enables young people to get together enough capital to rent a farm or to make a down payment on one. But clearly this problem is more troublesome than in many city occupations, where the ladders to success have many lesser rungs, useful for starting purposes. In farming, a late start or a beginning with inadequate capital may represent a waste of human resources.

Strains in noncommercial farming

The rapid growth of part-time and residential farming and the close intermingling of urban and rural interests have led to many stresses and strains in community life. Because of the varied characteristics of noncommercial farming in different places, problems of many kinds develop. More part-time and residential farming may help to solve some social problems by providing a larger income base for the support of community services. In low-income areas in which nearby industrial expansion has offered additional employment to surplus labor without bringing in additional population, this has undoubtedly been the case.

In other areas in which part-time and residential farming and rural residences have brought an influx of population, many problems related to taxation, and provision for roads, schools, churches, and other com-

5 See suggestions for facilitating improvement goals in agriculture, especially in reference to education, in the article by Sherman E. Johnson, "Technological Changes and the Future of Rural Life," *Journal of Farm Economics*, May 1950.

munity services have developed. The rights, interests, prejudices, and fears of the new and old portions of the population frequently come into conflict. Social pressures develop that are difficult to resolve.

Adjustments in these areas are closely connected with the great shift of population from central cities to suburban areas that has been general throughout the country since the end of World War II. The vast housing expansion in Suburbia has been accompanied by growing pains that have affected nearly every phase of local government and all community functions. In many suburban developments, the outer perimeter includes a measure of residential farming and some part-time farming.

In areas as far removed from one another as New England and southern California one can observe the merging of country and city on a grand scale. In the twilight zone between city and open country, commercial and part-time farms, factories, and residences are intermingled. The rapid growth of population in such places has frequently inflated real estate values with many unplanned and haphazard results and great losses to individuals. All the ills that Henry George decried are not offset by the random opportunities seized by unscrupulous individuals or accepted as windfalls by the more righteous. Frequently the reservation of a portion of windfall values to the public would have provided essential public services that have had to be financed through recourse to outmoded taxing devices.

Conservation of Human Resources

Much of the foregoing relates indirectly to the conservation of human resources. As a people, we have long been conscious of the need for conservation of natural resources. Secretary of Agriculture Ezra T. Benson, for example, said: "The Department of Agriculture recognizes a strong national program of soil, water, forest, and range conservation as one of the basic necessities of American agriculture." [6]

Perhaps we have not always been so fully conscious of an equal concern for the conservation of our human resources. Because these resources are people with basic rights and freedoms (at least in the Western World) that are not attached to inanimate resources, the problem of human conservation must be approached differently from that of physical resources. In a democratic society, we do not solve the problem by moving people around like machines. Solutions must be in terms that permit individuals to choose freely among alternatives on the basis of information and knowledge that is as complete as possible. To have meaning, freedom of choice must include freedom of access to information.

6 "Strengthening American Agriculture through Resource Conservation," *Office of the Secretary, U. S. Dept. of Agriculture, PA 237,* Nov. 1953.

The fact that we do not commonly place dollar signs against the human values in many situations concerning people causes us to under-rate the immense values that are actually involved. To take a familiar illustration, it is known that many advances in nutrition have been more quickly applied in animal feeding than in human nutrition. Yet who would say that the health of a cow or a hen is as significant as that of a person?

Before farmers can choose their individual farming programs wisely, they need to know more about the alternative production adjustments open to them in their localities and about the long-run prospects for markets for different products.[7] Measures for bringing about the best use of human resources need to be attacked along similar broad lines. To a considerable degree, the better use of physical resources represents a better use of human resources, but we need a deeper approach to human resources and a longer view than we are accustomed to take. Natural resources can be conserved and improved within rather well-defined limits. But man has infinitely greater possibilities. Conservation here means the opportunity to choose freely among alternatives that lead to better health and longer life, improved education and understanding, and ethical and esthetic appreciation—in short, freedom to develop wholesome, well-balanced lives in terms of all the material and immaterial values that give meaning to human existence.[8]

Conservation of human resources in the Western World outranks in the scale of real values all that can be said about conservation of natural resources. We may need to become more fully aware of this in order to direct our energies and surplus resources into the channels that will contribute most to permanent values.

---

[7] As an example see the suggestions for analysis of current economic change and for research in interregional competition set forth in: Ronald L. Mighell and John D. Black, *Interregional Competition in Agriculture,* Harvard University Press, Cambridge, 1951, especially pp. 292–314.

[8] How modern nutritional science may contribute to this process is suggested in the little book by H. C. Sherman, *The Science of Nutrition,* Columbia University Press, New York, 1943.

APPENDIX

Figure A-1. Map of the United States Showing Geographic Regions and Divisions Used by the Bureau of the Census

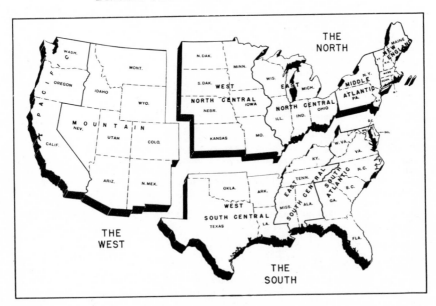

The census data used in this study are taken primarily from the regular and special reports and monographs of the 1950 Census of Agriculture. *Regular* reports consist almost entirely of tables with brief explanatory introductions and definitions. These are the "bare bones" of the census. *Special* census reports contain tables, charts, and some text. Usually they give detailed information concerning a specific subject. *Monographs* are primarily analytical and contain a number of tables and charts.

Regular reports of the 1950 Census of Agriculture appeared in 4 volumes as follows:

Volume I. Counties and State Economic Areas. This volume is published in thirty-four separate parts (one for each State, except for combinations of some smaller States) and includes all the general data.

Volume II. General Report. Statistics by Subjects. This is a large single volume; it contains summary data for States, geographic divisions, and the United States, by subjects.

Volume III. Irrigation of Agricultural Lands. Separate state reports contain data for counties and drainage basins and a summary for the United States. State reports are issued as eighteen separate parts of volume III.

Volume IV. Drainage of Agricultural Lands. This is issued in one part only; it contains state reports with statistics for counties and a summary for the United States.

Special reports are designated as parts of volume V and are as follows:

Part 1, "Horticultural Specialties," Sept. 1952
Part 2, "Multiple-Unit Operations," Nov. 1952
Part 3, "Ranking Agricultural Counties," Nov. 1952

Part 4, "Land Utilization—A Graphic Summary," Dec. 1952
Part 5, "Farm Tenure—A Graphic Summary," Dec. 1952
Part 6, "Agriculture 1950—A Graphic Summary," Dec. 1952
Part 7, "Irrigation 1950—A Graphic Summary," Dec. 1952
Part 8, "Farm-Mortgage Debt," Dec. 1952
Part 9, "Economic Class and Type of Farm—A Graphic Summary," Dec. 1952
Part 10, "Farms and Farm Characteristics by Economic Subregions," Dec. 1952.

In addition, an unnumbered special cooperative study entitled: "Farms and Farm People—Population, Income, and Housing Characteristics by Economic Class of Farm," June, 1953, was published jointly by the United States Departments of Agriculture and Commerce.

Parts 4, 5, 7, 8, and 9 of the numbered special reports were issued jointly as cooperative reports by the United States Departments of Commerce and Agriculture and involved participation by members of the staff of the Bureau of the Census and the Bureau of Agricultural Economics.

Census Monographs, of which this book is one, are described in the preface.

BIBLIOGRAPHY

1. Agricultural Research Service, "Farm Costs and Returns, 1953 (With Comparisons)," *U. S. Dept. Agr. Inf. Bul. 128, 1954.*
2. Allen, Frederick Lewis, *The Big Change,* Harper and Brothers, New York, 1952.
3. American Farm Bureau Federation, "Forward from Here with Farm Bureau—A Digest of 1953 Policies," Dec. 1952.
4. Bachman, Kenneth L., "Changes in Scale in Commercial Farming and Their Implications," *Journal of Farm Economics,* May 1952, pp. 157–172.
5. Bachman, Kenneth L. and Ronald W. Jones, "Sizes of Farms in the United States," *U. S. Dept. Agr. Tech. Bul. 1019,* 1950.
6. Boulding, Kenneth E., *The Organizational Revolution,* Harper and Brothers, New York, 1953.
7. Bureau of Agricultural Economics, "The Balance Sheet of Agriculture, 1953," *U. S. Dept. Agr. Inf. Bul. 115,* Sept. 1953.
8. Bureau of Agricultural Economics, "The Farm Income Situation," Sept.–Oct. 1953.
9. Bureau of the Census, *Annual Survey of Manufacturers, 1940–50.*
10. Bureau of the Census, *Statistical Abstract of the United States, 1953.*
11. Cochrane, Willard W., and Harlan C. Lampe, "The Nature of the Race Between Food Supplies and Demand in the U. S., 1951–75," *Journal of Farm Economics,* May 1953, pp. 203–222.
12. Cooper, Martin R., Glen T. Barton, and Albert P. Brodell, "Progress of Farm Mechanization," *U. S. Dept. Agr. Misc. Pub. 630,* 1947.
13. Davidson, R. D., "Federal and State Rural Lands, 1950," *U. S. Dept. Agr. Circ. 909,* 1952.
14. Fellows, I. F., G. E. Frick, and S. B. Weeks, "Production Efficiency on New England Dairy Farms. 2. Economics of Scale in Dairying—An Exploration in Farm Management Research Methodology," *Storrs Agr. Expt. Sta. Bul. 285,* 1952.
15. Galbraith, John K., *American Capitalism, The Concept of Countervailing Power,* Houghton Mifflin Co., Boston, 1952.
16. Griswold, A. Whitney, *Farming and Democracy,* Yale University Press, New Haven, 1952.
17. Grove, Ernest W., "Income of Farm-Operator Families in 1949," U. S. Dept. of Commerce and U. S. Dept. of Agriculture, *Farms and Farm People, A Special Cooperative Report,* 1953, pp. 23–44.
18. Harris, Marshall, "A New Agricultural Ladder," *Land Economics,* Aug. 1950, pp. 258–266.
19. Hathaway, Dale E., and Lawrence W. Witt, "Agricultural Policy: Whose Valuations?" *Journal of Farm Economics,* Aug. 1952, pp. 299–309.
20. Heady, Earl O., "Technical Scale Relationships and Farm Size Policy," *The Southern Economic Journal,* Jan. 1953, pp. 353–364.
21. Inman, Buis T., and Hilton E. Robison, "Changes in Farm Land Ownership," *Agricultural Economics Research,* Oct. 1953, pp. 87–94.
22. Johnson, Sherman E., "Changes in American Farming," *U. S. Dept. Agr. Misc. Pub. 707,* 1949.
23. Johnson, Sherman E., "Technological Changes and the Future of Rural Life," *Journal of Farm Economics,* May 1950, pp. 225–239.
24. Judkins, Jay, *National Associations of the United States,* U. S. Dept. of Commerce, 1949.
25. Kendrick, John W., and Carl E. Jones, "Gross National Farm Product in Constant Dollars, 1910–50," U. S. Dept. of Commerce, *Survey of Current Business,* Sept. 1951, pp. 13–19.
26. Leontief, Wassily W., "Input-Output Economics," *Scientific American,* Oct. 1951, pp. 15–21.
27. McElveen, Jackson V., "Low-Production Farms and the Low-Income Problem in Agriculture," U. S. Dept. of Commerce and U. S. Dept. of Agriculture, *Farms and Farm People, A Special Cooperative Report,* 1953, pp. 9–21.
28. McElveen, Jackson V., and Kenneth L. Bachman, "Low Production Farms," *U. S. Dept. Agr. Inf. Bul. 108,* 1953.
29. Mighell, Ronald L., and John D. Black, *Interregional Competition in Agriculture,* Harvard University Press, Cambridge, 1951.

30. Murphy, Donald R., "Winter on the Farm Is Cozier," *The New York Times Magazine*, Feb. 7, 1954.
31. President's Commission on Migratory Labor, *Migratory Labor in American Agriculture*, Washington, D. C., 1951.
32. Reagan, Barbara B., "Housing Facilities and Equipment, and Home Production Practices of Farm-Operator Families," U. S. Dept. of Commerce and U. S. Dept. of Agriculture, *Farms and Farm People, A Special Cooperative Report*, 1953, pp. 65–98.
33. Rozman, David, "Part-Time Farming in Massachusetts," *Mass. Agr. Expt. Sta. Bul. 266*, 1930.
34. Schultz, Theodore W., *The Economic Organization of Agriculture*, McGraw-Hill Book Co., Inc., New York, 1953.
35. Schumpeter, Joseph A., *Theory of Economic Development*, Harvard University Press, Cambridge, 1936.
36. Scoville, Orlin J., "Relationships Between Size of Farm and Utilization of Machinery, Equipment and Labor on Nebraska Corn-Livestock Farms," *U. S. Dept. Agr. Tech. Bul. 1037*, 1951.
37. Sherman, H. C., *The Science of Nutrition*, Columbia University Press, New York, 1943.
38. Sitler, Harry G., and R. T. Burdick, "The Economics of Sugar Beet Mechanization," *Colo. Agr. Expt. Sta. Bul. 411A*, 1953.
39. Smith, Mapheus, "Occupational Differentials in Physical Status," *American Sociological Review*, Feb. 1948, pp. 72–82.
40. Taylor, Carl C., *The Farmers' Movement 1620–1920*, American Book Co., New York, 1953.
41. Trelogan, Harry C., and Neil W. Johnson, "The Evitability of Technological Advance," *Journal of Farm Economics*, Nov. 1953, pp. 599–605.
42. United States Department of Agriculture, *Agriculture Statistics*, 1953 and earlier years.
43. United States Department of Agriculture, "Price Programs of the United States Department of Agriculture," *U. S. Dept. Agr. Inf. Bul. 13;* revised, Dec. 1953.
44. United States Department of Agriculture, *Report of the Administrator of Commodity Exchange Authority*, 1953.
45. United States Department of Agriculture, "Strengthening American Agriculture through Resource Conservation," Office of the Secretary, *U. S. Dept. Agr. PA 237*, 1953.
46. United States Department of Agriculture, "The Family Farm's Future," *U. S. Dept. Agr. PA 168*, 1951.
47. United States Selective Service System, "Physical Examination of Selective Service Registrants During Wartime," *Selective Service System Medical Statistics Bul. 3*, 1944.
48. White, Helen R., "Population in Farm-Operator Households," U. S. Dept. of Commerce and U. S. Dept. of Agriculture, *Farms and Farm People, A Special Cooperative Report*, 1953, pp. 45–64.
49. Wooten, H. H., "Major Uses of Land in the United States," *U. S. Dept. Agr. Tech. Bul. 1082*, 1953.

           AMERICAN AGRICULTURE

APPENDIX TABLES

TABLE A-1.—NUMBER OF FARMS, BY TYPE OF FARM, BY REGIONS, 1950

Type of farm	United States	North	South	West
All farms	5,379,250	2,267,083	2,650,803	461,364
All commercial farms	3,706,412	1,772,083	1,611,795	322,534
Cash-grain	430,389	318,356	62,455	49,578
Cotton	609,307	13,524	586,095	9,688
Other field-crop	409,421	21,780	374,617	13,024
Vegetable	46,415	18,053	18,740	9,622
Fruit-and-nut	82,178	16,784	18,979	46,415
Dairy	602,093	461,209	92,697	48,187
Poultry	175,876	94,413	54,071	27,392
Livestock [1]	806,080	526,298	209,296	70,486
General	494,285	281,770	172,636	39,879
Primarily crop	84,569	16,970	50,443	17,156
Primarily livestock	134,666	106,799	22,861	5,006
Crop-and-livestock	275,050	158,001	99,332	17,717
Miscellaneous	50,368	19,896	22,209	8,263
Noncommercial farms	1,672,838	495,000	1,039,008	138,830
Part-time	639,230	218,732	362,441	58,057
Residential	1,029,392	274,318	675,282	79,792
Unusual	4,216	1,950	1,285	981

[1] Livestock other than dairy and poultry.

TABLE A-2.—NUMBER OF FARMS, BY ECONOMIC CLASS OF FARM, BY REGIONS, 1950

Economic class	United States	North	South	West
All farms	5,379,250	2,267,083	2,650,803	461,364
All commercial farms	3,706,412	1,772,083	1,611,795	322,534
I	103,231	43,774	28,182	31,275
II	381,151	244,320	78,351	58,480
III	721,211	495,284	151,299	74,628
IV	882,302	486,088	324,191	72,023
V	901,316	331,254	510,317	59,745
VI	717,201	171,363	519,455	26,383
Noncommercial farms	1,672,838	495,000	1,039,008	138,830
Part-time	639,230	218,732	362,441	58,057
Residential	1,029,392	274,318	675,282	79,792
Unusual	4,216	1,950	1,285	981

TABLE A-3.—NUMBER OF COMMERCIAL FARMS BY TYPE OF FARM AND BY ECONOMIC CLASS OF FARM, UNITED STATES, 1950

Type of farm	All farms	Economic class					
		Class I	Class II	Class III	Class IV	Class V	Class VI
All commercial farms.	3,706,412	103,231	381,151	721,211	882,302	901,316	717,201
Cash-grain.............	430,389	13,763	74,102	127,744	109,815	68,041	36,924
Cotton................	609,307	11,246	27,242	44,972	91,377	195,921	238,549
Other field-crop........	409,421	4,845	13,073	37,316	114,317	143,253	96,617
Vegetables.............	46,415	3,074	4,858	6,743	9,248	10,824	11,668
Fruit-and-nut..........	82,178	5,249	11,022	15,491	18,929	19,924	11,563
Dairy.................	602,093	9,982	61,232	153,980	179,935	133,417	63,547
Poultry...............	175,876	8,648	22,531	28,427	34,030	43,033	39,207
Livestock [1]...........	806,080	36,853	122,905	189,087	176,580	152,708	127,947
General...............	494,285	5,204	38,384	110,854	138,940	121,490	79,413
Primarily crop........	84,569	2,329	6,940	12,364	19,071	23,727	20,138
Primarily livestock.....	134,666	551	7,871	31,451	41,906	32,736	20,151
Crop-and-livestock.....	275,050	2,324	23,573	67,039	77,963	65,027	39,124
Miscellaneous..........	50,368	4,367	5,802	6,597	9,131	12,705	11,766

[1] Livestock other than dairy and poultry.

TABLE A-4.—NUMBER OF COMMERCIAL FARMS BY TYPE OF FARM AND BY SIZE OF FARM, UNITED STATES, 1950

Type of farm	Farms	Size of farm						
		Under 10 acres	10–49 acres	50–99 acres	100–179 acres	180–259 acres	260–499 acres	500 and over
All commercial farms......	3,706,412	136,835	762,326	710,876	916,451	442,601	445,385	291,938
Cash-grain................	430,389	535	18,558	44,265	103,047	68,959	108,369	86,656
Cotton...................	609,307	22,565	280,278	130,400	94,593	32,858	32,097	16,516
Other field-crop..........	409,421	19,430	162,877	108,929	72,864	23,428	15,951	5,942
Vegetable................	46,415	4,240	20,160	10,411	6,609	2,000	1,678	1,317
Fruit-and-nut.............	82,178	9,950	40,483	14,642	9,118	3,142	2,757	2,086
Dairy....................	602,093	6,363	59,630	142,904	219,421	94,330	63,542	15,903
Poultry..................	175,876	42,663	56,666	35,814	25,615	7,763	5,483	1,872
Livestock [1].............	806,080	12,537	63,841	112,729	221,069	128,852	139,799	127,253
General..................	494,285	3,285	50,602	103,908	156,615	77,571	71,560	30,744
Primarily crop...........	84,569	570	14,696	20,962	21,738	9,467	10,180	6,956
Primarily livestock........	134,666	1,670	13,750	31,200	49,007	20,941	14,623	3,475
Crop-and-livestock........	275,050	1,045	22,156	51,746	85,870	47,163	46,757	20,313
Miscellaneous.............	50,368	15,267	9,231	6,874	7,500	3,698	4,149	3,649

[1] Livestock other than dairy and poultry

TABLE A-5.—NUMBER OF COMMERCIAL FARMS BY TYPE OF FARM AND BY TENURE OF OPERATOR, UNITED STATES, 1950

Type of farm	Farms	Tenure of operator			
		Full owners	Part owners	Man-agers	Tenants
All commercial farms................	3,706,412	1,812,999	729,275	19,705	1,144,433
Cash-grain............................	430,389	135,885	130,810	1,215	162,479
Cotton...............................	609,307	152,534	79,629	1,417	375,727
Other field-crop......................	409,421	158,649	58,948	789	191,035
Vegetable............................	46,415	25,134	10,844	451	9,986
Fruit-and-nut........................	82,178	66,569	8,171	2,459	4,979
Dairy................................	602,093	389,178	119,336	3,462	90,117
Poultry..............................	175,876	146,285	15,882	817	12,892
Livestock [1].........................	806,080	446,690	182,514	6,717	170,159
General..............................	494,285	251,330	118,288	1,332	123,335
Primarily crop......................	84,569	41,557	18,467	458	24,087
Primarily livestock..................	134,666	79,579	28,145	217	26,725
Crop-and-livestock..................	275,050	130,194	71,676	657	72,523
Miscellaneous........................	50,368	40,745	4,853	1,046	3,724

[1] Livestock other than dairy and poultry.

TABLE A-6.—NUMBER OF COMMERCIAL FARMS BY ECONOMIC CLASS AND BY SIZE OF FARM, UNITED STATES, 1950

Economic class	Farms	Size of farm						
		Under 10 acres	10–49 acres	50–99 acres	100–179 acres	180–259 acres	260–499 acres	500 and over
All commercial farms.....	3,706,412	136,835	762,326	710,876	916,451	442,601	445,385	291,938
I........................	103,231	3,679	5,778	4,768	8,960	9,068	22,288	48,690
II.......................	381,151	8,595	16,541	22,482	69,496	74,108	105,584	84,345
III......................	721,211	11,630	41,468	81,377	234,086	140,445	134,217	77,988
IV.......................	882,302	18,296	134,684	190,357	273,301	113,764	102,400	49,500
V........................	901,316	37,372	274,399	232,153	207,258	70,135	57,045	22,954
VI.......................	717,201	57,263	289,456	179,739	123,350	35,081	23,851	8,461

TABLE A-7.—NUMBER OF COMMERCIAL FARMS BY ECONOMIC CLASS AND BY TENURE
OF OPERATOR, UNITED STATES, 1950

Economic class	Farms	Tenure of operator			
		Full owners	Part owners	Man- agers	Tenants
All commercial farms.....	3,706,412	1,812,999	729,275	19,705	1,144,433
I.........................	103,231	37,548	40,211	6,619	18,853
II.........................	381,151	143,601	122,508	5,628	109,414
III.........................	721,211	313,727	188,401	4,881	214,202
IV.........................	882,302	441,516	174,428	1,475	264,883
V.........................	901,316	476,197	128,284	714	296,121
VI.........................	717,201	400,410	75,443	388	240,960

TABLE A-8.—THE INTERCHANGE OF GOODS AND SERVICES IN THE UNITED STATES BY MAJOR INDUSTRY GROUPS, 1947

[Data are rounded to nearest $0.1 billion. Items less than $0.05 billion are not shown]

Producing industry	Total gross output	Purchasing industry										
		Agriculture and fisheries	Food, fiber, and related manufactures	All other manufactures	Power, transportation, and communication	Trade	Finance, insurance, and real estate	Service industries	Inventory change (additions)	Foreign countries (exports to)	Government	Households
Total gross input (expenditure)	768.2	44.3	86.7	116.9	34.6	41.7	41.6	101.2	38.5	17.2	51.4	194.1
Agriculture and fisheries	44.3	10.9	18.1	1.3	—	—	—	1.2	1.0	1.3	0.6	9.9
Food, fiber, and related manufactures	86.7	2.6	20.6	4.1	0.4	0.8	0.5	12.9	2.2	3.4	1.4	37.8
All other manufactures	116.9	1.7	4.9	42.6	2.5	0.5	0.8	23.1	15.0	7.0	2.4	16.4
Power, transportation, and communication	34.6	1.1	2.9	5.2	3.3	1.2	3.9	3.9	0.5	2.5	1.4	8.7
Trade	41.7	1.4	1.4	1.5	0.5	0.2	0.8	5.5	2.5	1.0	0.1	26.8
Finance, insurance, and real estate	41.6	2.6	0.7	0.8	0.8	3.0	2.7	2.6	0.8	0.1	0.2	27.3
Service industries	101.2	0.6	6.6	11.7	2.8	6.3	5.7	8.8	15.9	0.2	10.4	32.2
Inventory change (depletions) [1]	4.4	2.7	0.8	0.5	0.7	—	—	0.4	—	—	—	—
Foreign countries (imports from)	9.5	0.7	3.4	1.9	—	—	0.1	0.1	—	—	1.3	1.3
Government	63.6	0.8	3.5	5.6	3.5	3.3	5.1	5.3	0.6	0.8	3.5	31.6
Households	223.7	19.2	23.8	41.7	20.1	26.4	22.0	37.4	—	0.9	30.1	2.1

[1] Includes private capital formation.

Source: Condensed from table in article by Wassily W. Leontief, "Input-Output Economics," *Scientific American*, Oct. 1951, pp. 15–21.

INDEX

Acreage allotments, 138
Adjustment, production, 135, 137–138, 164–165, 166
Agricultural Conservation Program Service, 139
Agricultural experiment stations, 6, 130
Agricultural extension service, 7, 129
Agricultural ladder, 95-96, 172
Agricultural Marketing Act of 1937, 136
Agricultural Marketing Act of 1946, 132
Agricultural Marketing Service, 133
Agricultural plant, complexity, 15
    resources included, 16–17
Agricultural research, 6–7, 130–132, 165
Agricultural Research Service, 133
Agriculture, place in economy, 9
    primary industry, 14
Allen, Frederick Lewis, 4
American Farm Bureau Federation, 124–125
American Gothic (Farmer and His Wife), 14

Bachman, Kenneth L., 45, 48, 50, 51, 64, 72, 114
"Balance Sheet of Agriculture," 17–18
Bank for Cooperatives, 134
Barriers of space removed, 141, 109–110, 160, 167
Barton, Glen T., 3
Beans, dry field, 81
Bee farms, 88
Beef, 86
Benson, Ezra T., 173
Black, John D., 33, 174
Böhm-Bawerk, 14
Boulding, Kenneth E., 119
Brodell, Albert P., 3
Burdick, R. T., 148
Bureau of Agricultural Economics, establishment of, 132
Bureau of Land Management, 139
Bureau of Public Roads, 132

Bureau of Reclamation, 139
Bureau of the Census, publications of the 1950 Census of Agriculture, 175–176

Capital rationing, 134
Cash-grain farms, 78–81, 91–92
Chain farming, 103
Chickens, 40–41
Citrus fruits, 81
Climate, economic, 29, 33
    natural, 28–32
Cochrane, Willard W., 131
Commercial farms, contrasted with noncommercial farms, 55
    distribution of, 58
    economic class by sales of farm products, 45
    number of, 44, 45
    trends in, 48–52
    value of products sold, 44, 45
Commodity Credit Corporation, 104–105, 136–137
Commodity Exchange Authority, 133
Commodity Stabilization Service, 136
Comparative advantage, climatic factors, 28–32
    economic factors, 29, 33
Conservation, 139
Consumer's dollar, farmer's share of, 11, 12
Consumption per capita, trends by food groups, 7–8
Contract farming, 103
Cooper, Martin R., 3
Cooperative associations, farmer, 125–127
    financing, 126
    marketing and purchasing, 126
    mutual fire insurance, 126
    production, 126
    rural health, 126
    telephone and electric, 126
Cooperative League of USA, 125

183